Peatlands

Peatlands

P.D. MOORE, B. Sc., Ph. D.
Botany department, School of Biological Sciences,
University of London King's College.

and

D.J. BELLAMY, B. Sc., Ph. D., F.L.S.
Botany Department, University of Durham.

Elek Science
London

© P. D. Moore and D. J. Bellamy 1974

First published in 1973 by
Paul Elek (Scientific Books) Ltd
54—58 Caledonian Road
London N1 9RN
ISBN 0 236 15473 7

Printed in Great Britain by
Unwin Brothers Limited
The Gresham Press, Old Woking,
Surrey, England
A member of the Staples Printing Group

Contents

To our wives

Preface

For many centuries peatlands have been a source of fascination to naturalists and scientists. When the itinerant John Leland passed through the peatlands of Central Wales in 1538 his comment was 'The pastures and montaynes of Cairdiganshire be so great that the hunderith part of hit roteth on the ground and makes sogges and quikke more by long continuance for lak of eting of hit'. His observation displays considerable ecological discernment, for he pinpoints those features of the peatland ecosystem which serve to differentiate it from all others and which have fired the imagination of generations of ecologists with an enthusiasm to understand the processes which Leland observed.

Peatlands are, by definition, unbalanced systems in which the rate of production of organic material by living organisms exceeds the rate at which these compounds are respired and degraded. The result is an accumulation of a proportion of this production (not always the 'hunderith part'!) as an organic deposit which we term peat. As the peat blanket thickens, the surface vegetation becomes insulated from underlying soils and rocks, and the resulting environmental changes are often accompanied by floristic changes which reflect the altered hydrology and chemistry of the peat surface. Peat producing ecosystems, or mires, are thus dynamic ecological entities, constantly changing, growing, spreading and eroding.

The peat itself is of fundamental interest to academic and industrialist alike. Within this humified mass of organic detritus is contained a wealth of information concerning the plants and animals which donated their bodies to its formation. From these subfossil, stratified remains it is possible to reconstruct the historical development of the mire and to elucidate the ecological processes which have been at work within it. In this way peat producing ecosystems deposit within their own accumulated substrate a detailed record of their own ontogeny.

Peat can be considered as an energy surplus stored within the ecosystem, resulting mainly from the relatively low levels of decomposer activity in situations where waterlogging leads to the development of anaerobic conditions. Industrial man is a glutton for energy and it is not surprising that he has expended much effort in tapping the energy resources of peatlands. Seventy power stations in the Soviet Union use peat as their energy source.

Peat possesses other properties which make it attractive to man, particularly those physical and chemical attributes which endue it with powers of water and nutrient retention when added to soil. Horticultural demand for peat is constantly rising and most of the peat harvested in Western Europe and the New World is used in this way.

In view of the ecological and economic importance of peatlands, it is natural that much research is being carried out throughout the world into various aspects of mires and peat production. In this book we hope to provide a survey of the results of some of this work and to present it in such a way that its meaning and significance will be apparent to the general reader. The literature reviewed is very considerable and, of necessity, we have been selective in the use we have made of it. Fairly extensive bibliographies are inserted at the end of each chapter which will enable the reader who seeks more detailed information to trace and consult the original published work.

Although the combined experience of the authors covers the mires of many parts of the world, it is inevitable that our experience is severely limited when one considers the vastness of the world's peatlands (exceeding 200 million hectares). Because of this our emphasis and the illustrations that we use are undoubtedly coloured by our limited experience. It is hoped, however, that the information contained within this book will prove of interest and value to those interested in peatlands throughout the world.

P.D.M., D.J.B., 1973

Chapter One

Geochemicals, Biogeochemicals and Ecosystems

As the earth cooled, chemical systems came into existence and the elements and compounds (geochemicals) now found in the earth's crust were formed. As cooling continued, compounds such as water were able to exist in the liquid state and the hydrosphere came into being.

At some point in the later part of the earth's history, chemical compounds developed that were capable of self replication, the energy necessary for the process of synthesis being derived from oxidoreduction reactions. The main constituents of these new chemical systems were carbon, nitrogen, oxygen, hydrogen, phosphorus and sulphur which, together with varying amounts of many of the other chemicals of the earth's crust, were channeled into the living process and a new global system of biogeochemical cycling was initiated.

Evolution was thus set in motion, a process through which the living biochemicals were to be carried to every part of the globe where water exists as a liquid and where geochemicals are available to that liquid medium.

A range of living forms gradually developed, each a product of evolution working within the limitations and opportunities of the abiotic environment. However, as the process continued new opportunities were created by the presence of other organisms and evolution responded to these opportunities. The most obvious biotic interaction is the evolution of food chains.

LIGHT — PHOTOSYNTHETIC PLANTS — HERBIVORES — CARNIVORES

The excess energy and biogeochemicals from each step and link in the chain provided opportunities for other types of organisms, the decomposers, which feed saprophytically on dead organic matter.

The vast range of living forms (organisms), now at least in part contained and classified within the Linnean system, are a result of this geochemical — biochemical — environmental interaction.

Thus every area of the biosphere contains a complex of organisms which are dependent upon each other and in part evolved in relation to

1

each other and their abiotic environment. Although it is almost impossible to delimit exact boundaries, such a working unit of biogeochemicals is called an ecosystem. 'Any area of nature that includes living organisms and non-living substances interacting to produce an exchange of materials between the living and the non-living part is an ecosystem' (Odum[1]).

As, with suitable modification, this could also be taken as a description of a living organism the idea of the ecosystem as a gigantic quasiorganism has arisen. An ecosystem has four main components, *energy, biogeochemicals, biota and abiotic.*

THE ENERGY

The bulk of the energy is entrained into the ecosystem through the process of photosynthesis, carried out by plants which contain the photoreceptive pigment chlorophyll. These are the primary producers of the system. All other components of the ecosystem can be classified with respect to energy into a number of trophic levels, each being one exchange step further from the energy source. Classification of the organisms on function, as primary producers, herbivores, carnivores and decomposers (see Figure 1.1) hides the real complexity

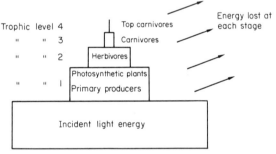

Figure 1.1. Simple trophic pyramid of energy.

of the food web which, from the carnivore step upwards, may consist of many substeps dependent upon size and other predator — prey relationships, possibly including actual predation on animals which feed as part of the decomposer chain. However, whether the stylised five step food chain, or the many stepped food web is considered, the following rules apply to each energy transfer:

1. Within each step in the chain energy is used in growth (increase in biomass, both living and dead) representing short term storage. The energy is stored in the form of carbohydrates, fats and proteins, this energy eventually passing to the decomposers.

2

2. Between each step there is a considerable loss of potential energy. The loss is made up of the following:
   a. Energy used in maintenance of the living systems.
   b. Energy used by the organisms in food searching, capture and digestion.
   c. Energy used in behavioural practices — migration, defence, burrowing, and nest building, courtship, etc. This energy represents the maintenance requirements 'respiration' of the ecosystem which is finally lost as heat to the environment.

BIOGEOCHEMICALS

These are basically geochemicals which are entrained into the ecosystem from the earth's crust and the atmosphere. The makeup of all living organisms (by weight) roughly approximates to carbon 20%, nitrogen 3%, oxygen 62%, hydrogen 10%, phosphorus 1·1% and lesser amounts of all the elements found in the earth's crust. Some of these, the 'trace elements', are essential to the living processes and structures; others, like mercury and arsenic, may be incorporated even though they have adverse effects on the living processes. These are best called 'toxicoids', because if they are present in sufficient quantity the living system will be impaired and the organism may die.

Carbon is mainly derived from atmospheric CO_2, or in aquatic ecosystems from dissolved bicarbonates; oxygen is also derived from the air and oxygen and hydrogen from water. All the other geochemicals come from the parent material from which the soil is derived and from which the water derives its solute load. Their availability is a function of their abundance and solubility. Owing to the rarity of nitrates in geological strata and their extreme solubility, a continuous supply of essential nitrates through the fixation of atmospheric nitrogen by specialised procaryotic organisms (blue-green algae and bacteria; Stewart[2]) is a feature of most ecosystems.

Certain groups of organisms show a marked deviation from the norm of biogeochemical constitution e.g. the Mollusca and Vertebrates, both of which have large amounts of calcium in their structural parts (shell and skeleton), and the Diatoms with their silica frustules. In these cases their potential performance may be limited by the supply of these key biogeochemicals.

THE BIOTA

The products of organic evolution are each fitted to their own abiotic and biotic environment, the climate, the supply of geochemicals and the flow of energy and their potential may be limited by any one

3

of these factors. Full classification of each member of the ecosystem using the Linnean binomial system allows indices of diversity to be calculated (Margalef[3]). However, until the role of each species within the ecosystem is known, these diversity indices are functionally meaningless.

The only real functional classification is one based on the actual biochemicals present, as it is this diversity which will determine the biochemical armoury of enzymes and metabolic systems needed in the ecosystem to facilitate degradation of the chemicals and hence energy flow. The three main types of biochemicals found in abundance in all natural ecosystems are shown in Table 1.1, together with the type of

TABLE 1.1

Biochemicals	Carbohydrates	Fats	Proteins
Calorific Value (Cal/g)	3·8	9·0	4·0
Enzymes	Carbohydrases	Lipases	Proteases

enzymes needed for their metabolism and their normal calorific value. All these represent short term storage products both for energy and geochemicals; and enzyme systems are present in the biochemical armoury of most ecosystems to deal with them. The main metabolic pathways for the release of energy from these compounds is oxidative metabolism through the glycolytic and organic acid pathways. These pathways are common to most organisms, and produce as end products of the process, carbon dioxide and water, both of which are raw materials for the process of photosynthesis. Under anaerobic conditions the end products of the metabolic processes are alcohol, organic acids etc. which, unless removed from the systems, inhibit further metabolism. Removal of any products of metabolism will depend upon diffusion aided by mass flow, or removal by recycling. Since the evolution of the process of photosynthesis, which releases oxygen into the atmosphere, anaerobic conditions will only exist within the atmosphere, hydrosphere or surface crust where mass flow is absent and diffusion limited. Under such conditions the products of partial metabolism must accumulate.

Of all the main biochemicals found in the ecosystem, the least tractable to metabolism are, as might be expected, the structural carbohydrates like cellulose, chitin and lignin. Few of the larger more complex organisms have for instance cellulases and most herbivores depend on the flora of procaryotic organisms (bacteria), which inhabit their digestive tracts, in order to obtain the energy from these structural compounds. Lignin is of interest in the respect that not only is it an abundant constituent of the xylem of most higher plants, but its chemical structure includes a phenol ring and lignin

4

therefore has bacteriostatic properties.

These substances will therefore accumulate in the soil, or in detrital deposits in water bodies, where they will be broken down by microorganisms which have the necessary enzyme systems.

Consideration of the decomposition of cellulose will suffice to indicate the complexity of the decomposer chain. The decomposition of cellulose is brought about by the following organisms living in the soil, fungi, actinomycetes and bacteria such as *Clostridium, Cellulomonas, Celluvibrio, Cytophaga* etc. In the soil the 'food stuffs' and microorganisms are so well mixed that it is impossible to say exactly what reaction and interaction takes place. There are both symbioses (mutual help), antibioses (antagonism) and other complex interactions. Cellulose is usually decomposed by the combined and reciprocal action of a variety of organisms (Frobisher[4]).

The products and byproducts of this slow decay in the soil are called humus (the dead organic fraction of the soil). A 'good soil', that is 'good' in the agricultural sense, usually contains a lot of humus. Humus not only helps to hold water in the soil by adsorption and imbibition onto the humic complexes, which are in the main colloidal, but it also interacts with the geochemical constituents of the parent substrate from which the soil is being formed. This interaction produces aggregations of mineral particles and humus which give structure to the soil. The structural units or crumbs are irregular and therefore have spaces between them which allow free drainage of rain water through the soil and hence more efficient aeration of the upper soil profile in which aerobic organisms can thrive. Soil is thus an important and integral part of terrestrial ecosystems, being not only the source of the bulk of the geochemicals but also the area and main seat of the final processes of the food chain decomposition. The gradual processes of decomposition replenish the supply of biogeochemicals to the living system.

THE ABIOTIC

The complex of environmental factors which make life possible on the surface of the earth are best considered under four main headings.

1. *The geochemicals* of the parent material, which by the processes of mechanical, chemical and biological weathering are gradually incorporated into a structured soil, or pass into solution and hence into the hydrological cycle.

2. *The hydrological cycle* and especially rainfall supplying water to the biota, the soil reservoir and to the process of mechanical and chemical weathering.

5

3. *The climate,* especially infrared radiation heating the atmosphere, the earth's surface and the biota, the most important feature being the maintenance of temperatures between which water can exist as a liquid and living macromolecules are not denatured. Within this range an increase of $10°C$ roughly doubles the rate of most biochemical reactions.
4. *The gases* of the atmosphere, especially O_2, CO_2, N_2 and water vapour all of which are important biogeochemicals. Linked to this is the wind, adding flow to all processes of atmospheric diffusion. These, together with light energy were the 'five factors (soil, temperature, water, atmosphere and energy) affecting vegetation' described by Lundegardh[5].

The enormous complexity of interaction of these factors is obvious and, in order to allow further discussion, it is suggested that the abiotic complex is best regarded as a template, the intimate construction of which will determine the type of ecosystem which can be formed and the biota which can play a part in that ecosystem.

An ecosystem may therefore be regarded as the interaction between the incident energy, the abiotic and the biotic in a stated area over a stated interval of time.

THE INTERACTIONS

1. Utilisation of energy by the life processes of the biota, growth, salt uptake, feeding, excretion, secretion, etc., are the component mechanisms of geochemical entrainment and cycling, especially that of water, carbon and nitrogen. All these processes must therefore have marked effects on the geochemical makeup of the abiotic template.
2. Storage of energy as standing crop (biomass) has marked effects on the climate near the ground, smoothing out the fluctuation of temperature and humidity, creating niches for the growth of other plants and of animals, extending the ecosystem vertically and in so doing exploiting more space and deeper supplies of raw materials.
3. Storage of energy as humus will affect the process of chemical weathering of the parent material and hence the composition and the structure of the developing soil. It will especially increase the retention capacity of the soil for water and other geochemicals.
4. Storage of energy as peat can gradually fill a body of water, changing the template very radically.

All the time there is energy fixed by photosynthesis which is excess to the maintenance requirements of the ecosystem. That is, all the time the gross photosynthesis of the ecosystem is greater than the gross respiration, this excess energy will be stored in the form of standing crop, humus or peat. The ecosystem is in positive energy balance and the abiotic template will be changed. When these changes are sufficient to cause a change in the biotic component of the system, succession (*sensu* Clements[6]) is said to have taken place.

Succession is a linked change of the biotic and the abiotic components of an ecosystem brought about by the utilisation and storage of energy by the ecosystem.

The process will continue until some factor stabilises the annual energy budget, so that all the energy fixed by the process of photosynthesis is in unit time used up in the maintenance of the ecosystem, (gross ecosystem photosynthesis = gross ecosystem respiration). At this point the template and the biotic community stabilise as abiotic change and hence succession slows down and comes to a halt. The process is shown diagrammatically in Figure 1.2.

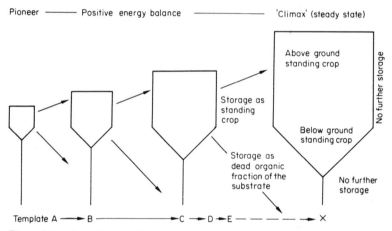

Figure 1.2. *Basic diagram of succession.*

The exact point of stabilisation will depend upon what factor, climatic, edaphic, biotic, anthropogenic, etc., limits the process. For example, fire, whether natural or manmade will dissipate the energy stored in the standing crop and stable heathland may result, likewise concentrated grazing can produce stable grassland ecosystems.

In all except the highest latitudes and altitudes and the driest climate, natural succession passes towards some form of structured ecosystem, the most complex being layered forest systems which are typified by large standing crops and a more or less closed cycle of biogeochemistry.

The Zonation of Vegetation on a World Scale.

Tundra, taiga, mixed boreal forest, subtropical forest, tropical rain forest are the contemporary terminal phases of the process of succession set against the background of macroclimate; the *status quo* not only of organic evolution (the evolution of biota) but of the development of complexes of biota working together within the limitations and potentials of the environment.

This book concerns one specialised type of ecosystem which is found throughout all except the driest macroclimatic regions of the world. This is the peat producing ecosystem or mire.

Peat is partially decayed organic matter, mainly of plant origin. Theoretically any ecosystem can form peat if given the right template condition; few actually do owing to their intolerance of this template condition.

REFERENCES

1. ODUM, E.P. *Fundamentals of Ecology.* Saunders, U.S.A. 546 (1959).
2. STEWART, W.D.P. *Nitrogen Fixation in Plants.* Athlone Press, London, 168 (1966).
3. MARGALEF, R. *Perspectives in Ecological Theory.* Univ. Chicago Press, 111 (1968).
4. FROBISHER, M. *Fundamentals of Microbiology.* Saunders & Co. Phil., (1953).
5. LUNDEGÅRDH, H. *Klima und Boden in ihrer Wirkung auf das Pflanzenleben.* Gustav Fischer Verlag Jena (1954).
6. CLEMENTS, F.E. *Plant succession, an analysis of the development of vegetation.* Publ. Carnegie Inst. Wash., **242**, 1-512 (1916).

Chapter Two

Templates of Peat Formation

Precipitation falling on the earth's surface flows under the action of gravity down towards the sea. The increasing water mass possesses kinetic energy which produces work in the form of scouring, erosion and dissolution of the solid materials of the catchment. The rate of dissipation of the energy will depend on the geology and the geomorphology of the catchment and will be reflected in the competency of the water body to transport the products of erosion. Competency (Chebotarev[1]) is the ability of a stream to transport in terms of the dimensions of particles. Any surface feature which reduces the rate of dissipation of the energy, that is reduces the competency of the water body, to a level where sediments are no longer carried by traction, can constitute a template for peat formation. Such features include all forms of natural basins from valley heads to those situated in deltaic flood plains. It is therefore clear that the most important factors determining the type of mire system which will develop will be the hydrological balance of the basin and the amount of minerals in solution.

THE HYDROLOGICAL TEMPLATE

The water balance equations of these mire templates are simple:

$$INFLOW = OUTFLOW + RETENTION$$

Peat growth is initiated within the retention volume, the peat acting as an inert body displacing its own volume of water. Peat growth of this type can only continue up to a point at which the surface of the peat reaches the level at which water drains from the reservoir. Beyond this point the peat no longer acts as an inert mass but as an active reservoir which holds a volume of water against drainage. As no clear distinction between these peat phenomena can be found in the literature the terms 'primary', 'secondary' and 'tertiary' are proposed and are defined below.

Primary peats and hence primary mire systems are those formed in basins or depressions. Their development reduces the surface retention (synonym for depression storage — Chebotarev[1]) of the reservoir. Mire systems of this type can be found in all except the most hot and arid areas of earth.

Secondary peats and hence secondary mire systems are those which develop beyond the physical confines of the basin or depression, the peat itself acting as a reservoir and increasing the surface retention of the landscape unit.

Tertiary peats and hence tertiary mire systems are those which develop above the physical limits of the ground water, the peat itself acting as a reservoir holding a volume of water by capillarity up above the level of the main ground water mass draining through the landscape. The tertiary peat reservoir acts as a 'perched water table' fed by the precipitation falling directly on it.

Mire systems producing secondary and tertiary peats are only found in areas where the macroclimate is favourable. Their distribution is therefore limited by macroclimate and the various types of mire complex in which secondary and tertiary peat is formed show a distinct zonation with respect to macroclimatic factors on a global scale.

One type of mire is difficult to place in any one of these categories, that is mires which form over artesian spring heads. The peat in this case acts as a reservoir containing the spring water. Upward growth of the peat is however limited by the height of the hydrostatic head of the spring acting within the containing mass of peat and vegetation. Spring mires thus occupy an intermediate position between the definitions, a full description of spring mires is given on page 80.

THE CLIMATIC TEMPLATE:
CLIMATIC LIMITS OF PEAT DEVELOPMENT

The Primary Mires

Mire systems have been described from many parts of the tropics, but the majority of them are found in mountainous areas which have predominantly wet and humid climates. Extensive lowland primary mires are restricted in the subtropics and tropics to deltaic and estuarine situations where they merge with the coastal mangrove swamps. The best known example is the Everglades of Florida (Davis[2]) which has many features of similarity with the coal forming systems which were widespread during the Carboniferous period (Spackman *et al*[3]). It was Eurey[4] who first pointed to the fact that the coal swamps should be regarded as enormous 'peat bogs' (mires) in which the active peat formers were giant Pteridophytes, in contrast to the delicate mosses and herbs which are the main active 'ingredients' of contemporary peat formation. There is little doubt that they were primary tropical or subtropical coastal mires. Contemporary tropical coastal peat deposits being formed from trees, mainly members of the *Dipterocarpaceae*, have been described from Assam (Anderson[5]).

Figure 2.1 includes the climatic diagram (Walters and Lieth[6]) for the appropriate area of Florida, namely Tampa. The key feature which restricts mire development is the dry season, coupled with high temperatures which result in high evapotranspirational loss of the surface waters.

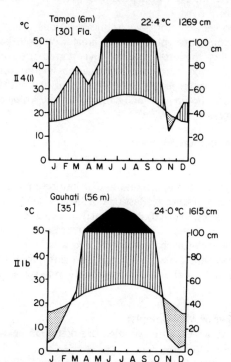

Figure 2.1. Walters climate diagrams for the two areas of Florida and Assam from which primary and secondary mire systems have been described. Dotted areas indicate dry periods. For full explanation of the diagrams, see Figure 2.5. (Redrawn after Walters and Lieth[6])

Ephemeral mire systems have been described from Gauhati in Assam (Bellamy[7]) where there is a much longer and more pronounced dry season. The peat forming communities consist of species which can aestivate over the dry period and can develop and grow very rapidly as

11

the depressions fill with water at the onset of the rains. The productivity of the vegetation is high, netting more than 9 g dry weight/m^2/day and a layer of organic matter begins to accumulate. The peaty deposit however lasts only as long as the pool; as the pool evaporates the peat dries and is blown away.

It is therefore easy to understand why peat development is restricted in hot dry climates to estuarine coastal sites receiving a more or less continuous drainage inflow throughout the year which keeps the basins filled with water.

Passing to cooler and more evenly humid regions, primary and secondary peat development is possible in a greater range of basin sites very roughly following the order, deltas, river terraces, open lake basins, closed lake basins and valley heads: that is passing up from the sink to the source on the watershed. It is therefore clear that both precipitation and evaporation should be included in the hydrological equations of the mire template

INFLOW + PRECIPITATION = OUTFLOW + EVAPORATION + RETENTION

The Tertiary Mires

Figure 2.2 shows the approximate distribution of the main types of mire system found in Europe. Passing northwards and northwestwards a series of zones are delimited, within each of which a new type of tertiary mire complex may be found. The lines represent very approximately the southern limits of each type, north and west of the lines each type may be found within the all other zones except that of the palsamires. However even in the palsamire zone primary mire systems can be widespread.

The Major Types of Mire Complex

The major types of mire complex are described below and a basic synonymy is given in Table 2.1.

Zone 1 Primary and secondary mires only are present.

Zone 2 Flat tertiary mires in open basins. These are formed on the flooded terraces of deltas, rivers and major streams and in shallow open lakes. The peat reservoir is only slightly raised above the level of the groundwater of the basin and is flat topped or very slightly convex.

The example shown in Figure 2.3. is part of the Murnauer Moor complex in Bavaria. The morphological basin is well supplied with groundwater throughout the year and the tertiary peat reservoir is relatively very small.

Zone 3 Flat tertiary mires in closed basins. Peat deposits filling basins

12

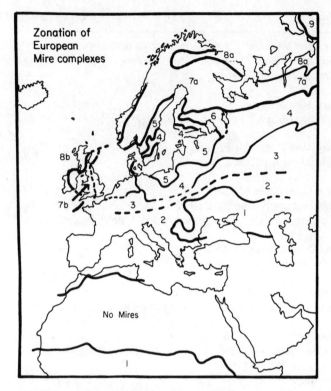

Figure 2.2. Map showing the approximate zonation of the mires of Europe. The lines represent very approximately the south/eastern limits of each type

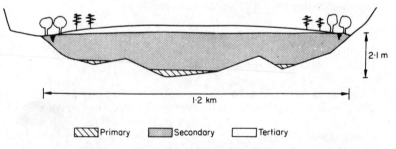

▨▨▨ Primary   ▦▦ Secondary   ☐ Tertiary

Figure 2.3. Section across part of a tertiary mire complex of Zone 2. Note that the mire has developed in an open valley and the very flat tertiary reservoir. The tertiary reservoir has been exaggerated in the diagram

TABLE 2.1 PARTIAL SYNONYMY FOR MIRE COMPLEX TYPES

Primary and Secondary Mire Systems of Zone 1
Flachmoore (Bulow[43]) Uberschwemungsmoore (Weber[44]) Valley Bogs (Kulczynski[16]) Fens (Tansley[19]).

Tertiary Mire Systems
Hochmoore (Bulow[43]) Raised Bog (Kulczynski[16]).

Tertiary Valley Mires of Zone 2
Flach Hochmoore (Bulow[43]).

Tertiary Basin Mires of Zone 3
Waldhochmoore (Weber[44]), Beckenmoore (Bulow[43]), Karst Raised Bogs and Continental Raised Bogs (Kulczynski[16]), Basin Bogs (Fraser[45]).

Plateau Domed Mires of Zone 4
Seenplatten Hochmoore (Ruuhijarvi[12]).

Concentric Domed Mires of Zone 5
Echte Hochmoore (Bulow[43]); Baltic Raised Bog (Kulczynski[16]).

Excentric Mires of Zone 6
Kermi Hochmoore (Ruuhijarvi[12]) and Excentric Raised Bogs.

Aapamires, Zone 7a
Aapamoore (Ruuhijarvi[12]) String Bogs & Patterned Fens (Sjörs[27]).

Palsamires, Zone 8a
Palsamoores (Ruuhijarvi[12]): Hugel Moores (Bulow[43]).

Unconfined Arctic Mires, Zone 9
Arktische Moore (Bulow[43]): in part unconfined Muskeg (Radforth[22]) Thermal Blanket Mire (Bellamy et al[40])

Ridge Raised Mires, Zone 7b
Continental Ridge Raised Bogs (Kulczynski[16]), Red Bogs (Praeger[47]).

Blanket Mires, Zone 8b
Terrainbedeckendenmoore (Bulow[43]) Blanket Bogs (Tansley[19]).

which have neither inflow nor outflow streams. The tertiary peat reservoir is raised only slightly above the ground water level of the basin. The example shown in Figure 2.4 is a mire in the Mazurian lake district of Poland. The growth mechanism of this type of peat deposit is of interest.

Peat development is initiated around the edges of the basin, the primary mire gradually growing inwards, filling the basin until finally the lake disappears, as the tertiary reservoir develops. In those areas where the climate allows the development of coniferous mire forest (see page 30) natural forestation follows the centripetal development of the peat. The youngest, stunted pioneer trees are found ringing the central lake remnant, the trees become taller and more mature towards the edge of the basin giving the forest a concave skyline (see Figure 2.4a)

The pioneer mire communities which gradually encroach over the lake may be in actual fact floating. The floating living mat of mire vegetation and the floating peats are called by the very descriptive name of schwingmoore in the German language. In deep steep sided basins, the whole system, including the mature pine forest, can be floating suspended over deep water. One very good example of this is the Chartley Moss National Nature Reserve in Staffordshire, England where the mature forest is suspended in places over more than 10 m of water.

Completely floating mires of this type must be classified as primary, due to the fact that the surface of the mire conforms and fluctuates with the water table of the reservoir. The distinction between secondary and tertiary mires in both zones 1 and 2 is very tenuous and accurate levelling and hydrological studies must be undertaken to demonstrate the existence of a tertiary peat reservoir which may be represented by a rise of no more than 10 cm in many hundreds of metres.

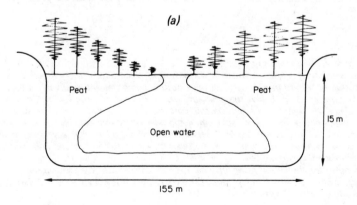

(a)

Peat   Peat

Open water

15 m

155 m

15

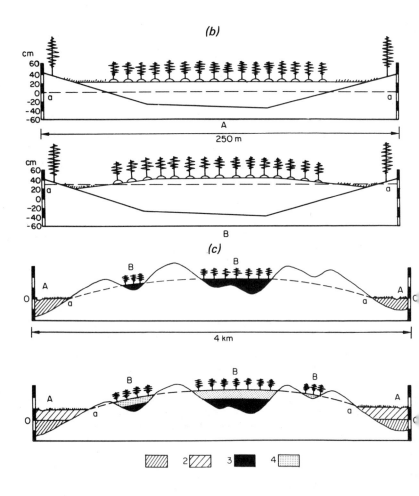

Figure 2.4.   Sections of zone 3 mires
(a) Section of a mire formed in a deep steep sided basin. (b) A shows a cross-section of a mire in summer, the mire outline being flat and the water table a (a being some 20 cm below the peat surface). B shows a cross-section of the mire in spring. The water saturated central part of the peat mass has expanded and emerged above the water table while the lagg where the peat layer is thinner is flooded. (c) shows the growth mechanism of these mires. Primary mires in the adjacent valleys grow thicker as the secondary reservoir builds up. This causes a corresponding rise in the water table a-a of the watershed thus providing a growth impulse for the closed mire systems. Legend: (1) old primary and secondary peat (2) newly formed secondary peat (3) tertiary peat (4) newly formed tertiary peat (Redrawn after Kulczynski[16])

When development is complete, that is when the original lake is completely filled, the forest canopy rapidly becomes uniform. Growth of the tertiary reservoir may however still continue, the mechanism proposed by Kulczynski is shown in Figure 2.4b and is described below.

Where such mire systems are developed in closed basins on permeable substrata continued growth of secondary mire systems in the adjacent drainage axes (adjacent valleys) will bring about a gradual rise in the water table of the closed basins, allowing continued upward growth of the tertiary reservoirs.

It is easy to see that if a series of adjacent basins are of the right morphology then this synchronous growth can cause coalescence of the adjacent mire systems to produce what Kulcynski terms 'ridge raised bogs' (see Figure 2.4c).

Kulczynski stresses the fact that factors such as substrate permeability and area of the mire system may in part override macroclimate in determining the type of mire complex which will develop in certain regions.

One of the earliest reference to these small basin mires is in Plot's[8] Natural History of Staffordshire published in 1686. He recounts the discovery during peat cutting operations of well preserved trunks of birch and pine trees. He suggested that when the trees in the depressions were first felled, water loss was so reduced that the basins filled with water and the peat began to form. However erroneous Plot's theory may be, there is little doubt that many of the small basin mires found in Britain began to form during the Neolithic period when man was beginning to have his first impact on the forested landscape. Basin mires were well known to certain groups of primitive man, for they were certainly the favourite type of mire selected for sacrificial burials by the bog cultures of Europe (Glob[9]) the most famous being Tollund man, and the importance of these findings to archaeology lies in the remarkable preservative powers of the peat.

Zone 4 Plateau mires. These have large tertiary peat systems developed as flat plateaux with a relatively steep marginal slope. Mire forest is often a feature of the marginal slope. Plateau mires may be distinguished from those of Zone 5 by the fact that the surface features of hummocks- and hollows are not aligned in a concentric pattern (see below) except near the marginal slope.

Zone 5 Concentric domed mires. These are in their typical form great convex masses of peat, the tertiary reservoirs being in the form of domes or cupolas of peat which grow up above the fluctuations of the original ground water table. They can develop both in open and closed basins. In the former the inflow stream continues to flow around one or both margins of the basin. Mire complexes of this type are so common in certain parts of Sweden that there is a word in the Swedish language for the wetter area which is subject to ground water flow and which separates the mire proper from the mineral edge of the basin. The word is lagg and as it has such a specific meaning it has been adopted as a scientific term.

The tertiary peat reservoir can be enormous, covering many square kilometres and rising to heights greater than 6 m. The cupola has always been regarded as a sponge-like mass, the water in which is held by capillarity against gravity. The whole complex grows in unison, as more primary peat is laid down in the lagg the base level of the ground water will rise, thus allowing the whole system to continue its upward growth. The actual height to which the cupola can grow above the ground water table in the lagg is a function of the area of the mire and the precipitation/evaporation balance of the region. The concept of the mire complex (Cajander[10]) is therefore easily understood, each part of the complex mire system developing and growing together in unison,

Figure 2.5 shows the range of climatic types which characterise the zone of domed mires.

The example shown in Figure 2.6 is the Wurzacher Ried in Southern Germany which was first described by Bertsch[11]. The Wurzacher Ried demonstrates two important phenomena. The first is that it lies well south of the main zone 4. It is however situated at 650 m above sea level in the montane climate of the foothills of the Allgau Alps. The climate diagram for the region shows that the main period of rainfall is during the summer months, that is during the main growth period of the peat forming vegetation. During the drier winter when an adverse precipitation/evaporation balance could exist the mire surface will be frozen for long periods and/or be under a protective blanket of snow.

The second feature is the concentric arrangement of the mire communities around the most elevated part of the cupola which includes an open pool. The whole pattern is very reminiscent of the centripetal development of closed basin mires.

There seems little doubt that they are 'genetically' related and that a concentric floating mire can, if it is of the right dimensions and is situated in a favourable climate, develop into a concentric domed mire carrying the lake remnant upwards. Pool systems are common features of concentric mire complexes in Fennoscandia. Plate 2.1 is an aerial photograph of a concentric mire complex in Sweden. The concentric pattern is here accentuated by the alignment of the mire surface features, such as the pools and hummocks, across the main direction of slope of the cupola. A fuller appraisal of the hummock, hollow pool complex is given on page 151.

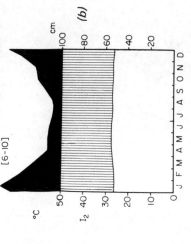

Kuching (26 m) 26·8 °C 3968 cm
[6-10]

(b)

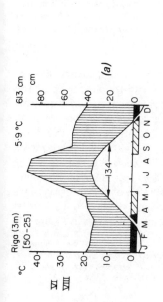

Riga (3m) 5·9 °C 613 cm
[50-25]

(a)

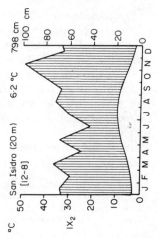

San Isidro (20 m) 6·2 °C 798 cm
[12-8]

(c)

Figure 2.5. Climatic diagrams (Walters and Lieth[6]) of areas from which domed tertiary mires have been described. (a) The Baltic region where domed mires are best developed (b) Sarawak where domed forested mires are found (c) South America where such mires are widespread.

Explanation. The bottom line shows mean monthly temperatures, the top line means monthly rainfall. The period with excessive rainfall is shown hatched, very high rainfalls are shown in black shading. Along the bottom of the diagram, solid bar shows months with mean temperature below 0°C, the hatched bar indicates months with frost. Along the top of the diagram is the name of the station and its altitude and below, in brackets, is shown the number of years for which the data have been collected. Also shown is the mean annual temperature and mean annual rainfall. Roman numerals beside each diagram denote climate type (Walters and Lieth[6]).

19

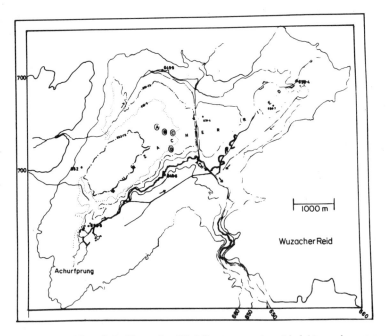

Figure 2.6. Map of the Wurzacher Ried. Contours and spot heights are in metres. (A) central open Sphagnum cuspidatum *of residual pool (B) zone with lawns of* Sphagnum papillosum, S. magellanicum *(C) zone with dominant* S. fuscum *(D) zone with* S. magellanicum *and developing mire forest.*

For reasons which will become obvious it is in some cases difficult to distinguish between the mires of zone 4 and those of zone 5. The zone boundary is therefore a very tenuous one. However, when developed in their typical form, distinct differences between the two types can be seen. Concentric domed mires are usually found with a foundation of primary peat formed in basins which are more or less horizontal, that is there is very little difference between the heights of the inflow and outflow streams. The secondary peat reservoir therefore builds up uniformly over the horizontal surface of the primary peats. *Zone 6 Eccentric domed mires.* These have their foundations in basins and especially basin complexes of the type shown in Figure 2.7.

Plate 2.1 Concentric domed mire. The length of this mire is 2.2 km. Note the basic concentric arrangement of the pools, especially around the more northerly dome. The southern part shows the more eccentric arrangement of pools and hummocks (By kind permission of H. Sjörs and the R.Sw.A.F.)

20

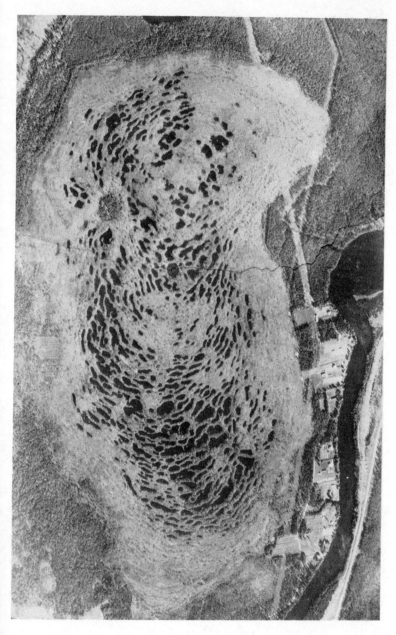

21

The primary peats begin to develop, each with a horizontal surface conforming with the water levels in the basin units. These primary peats form nuclei for the development of the tertiary peat reservoir which overflows the morphological basins to produce a cupola which appears

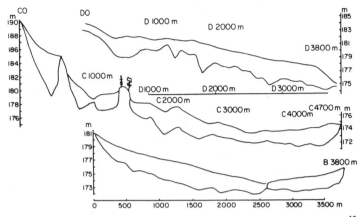

Figure 2.7.   Profiles of an eccentric mire complex (Redrawn after Ruuhijarvi[12])

to hang on the side of the valley. The opposing forces of upward growth of the peat and gravity acting downslope on the waterlogged mass, coupled with the fact that the upslope edge of the mire is in the most advantageous position in relation to water supply, produces an eccentric dome of peat. The surface features, hummocks, hollows and pools become aligned in relation to the highest point of the cupola which is closest to the upper margin of the mire. These features are often accentuated to give elongated structures which may be more than a metre in height and many metres long, each arranged across the main angle of slope of the cupola. These large elongated hummocks are called kermis in Finnish and are often separated by elongated sinuous pools, the whole providing a striking pattern when seen from the air.

   Plate 2.2 is an aerial view of part of Claish Moss which is an eccentric domed mire complex situated well outside of the zone 5 climatic zone, in Western Scotland.

   The main area in which this type of mire complex is found is in the

Plate 2.2.   Part of Claish Moss, Scotland, an eccentric mire complex. Note how the complex is formed on a slope between the lake on the left and the high ground on the right, also the excentric pattern of pools and hummocks lying at right angles to the slope (Crown copyright reserved. Reproduced by kind permission of the Controller of H.M.S.O.)

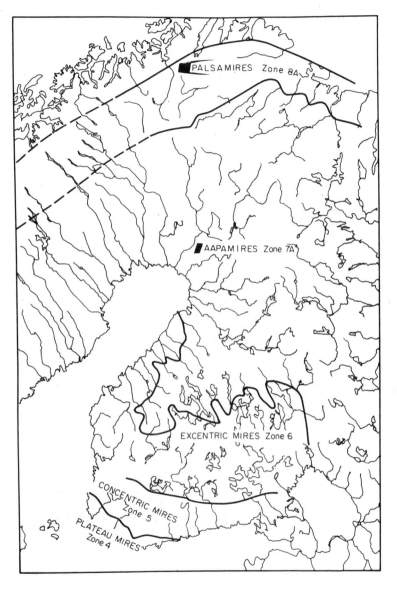

Figure 2.8. Map showing the distribution of the main types of mire complex found in Finland (Redrawn after Ruuhijarvi[12])

24

North Karelian region of Finland. The map in Figure 2.8 shows the zonation of the mire complex types in Finland. Ruuhijarvi[12] states in his paper (from which Figure 2.8 is taken) that although the zonation does exist it is not at all clear cut. The reason is that with the three mire complex types of zones 4, 5 and 6, topography and especially the slope and area of the catchment which supplies water to the developing mire play some part in determining which mire type develops. Ruuhijarvi[12] and Tolonen[13] both discuss the relative importance of climatic and topographic control of these three mire types. The evidence certainly points to macroclimate as exerting the major control. It seems safe to conclude that passing north and west the increasing oceanicity of the climate allows the peat reservoirs to develop further beyond the confines of the primary peat deposit both vertically and horizontally.

There is from about this zone onwards a distinct dichotomy of mire complex types, one series which will be numbered zones 7a, 8a and 9 are found passing into the arctic climate of northern Fennoscandia, the other passing westwards to the climate of the atlantic seaboard, these will be numbered zones 7b and 8b.

Zone 7a Aapamires. In their typical form aapamires consist of very large expanses of mire in which the excentric doming of the peat is less well marked, in fact the tertiary reservoir is almost lost. Perhaps the best features which distinguish aapamires are their larger size and the type and alignment of their surface features. The hummock and hollow systems are accentuated and are arranged at right angles to the surface slope of the mire as shown in Plate 2.3 and Figure 2.9. Attenuation of the hummocks produces great chains or ridges which are called strings and are separated by wide elongate pools, called flarks. The flarks are often so wide and deep that the only way to traverse the mire,

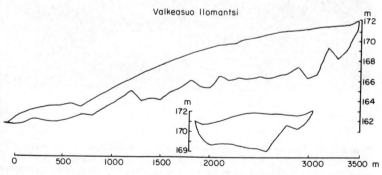

Figure 2.9. Profile of an Aapamire complex (Redrawn after Ruuhijarvi[12])

25

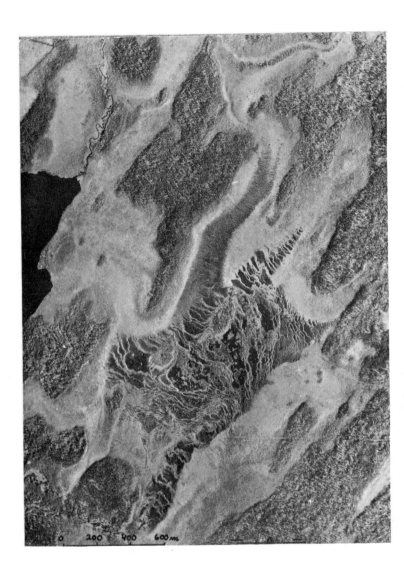

Plate 2.3.   *Aapamire complex, Finland. Note the arrangement of pools and hummock strings at right angles to the direction of the slope, also the similarity of some parts of the complex to excentric domed mires (By kind permission of R. Ruuhijarvi)*

especially during periods of snow melt, is to walk along the string ridges.

There is little doubt that the long cold winters and shorter growing periods in these more northerly latitudes play some role, as yet unknown (see pages 37-40), in the aapamire template. An important feature would appear to be that the whole surface must be frozen throughout the winter, thus reducing evapotranspirational loss. This relationship will be further investigated later in this chapter.

Zone 8a Palsamires. Study of the airform pattern of any aapamire usually reveals areas where the strict linearity of flarks and strings is lost. There is some evidence that towards the north of the aapamire zone this breakdown in the strict patterning becomes more widespread, the mire expanse consisting of large interlocking plateaux set in a matrix of interlocking flarks.

It is on the larger of the plateaux that the palsa mounds which give the most northerly mire type its name are found.

Palsas are large mounds of peat which average about 3 m high and about 20 − 100 m in breadth and length. Some are however much larger, rising to a height of over 10 m.

The climatic limits of the palsamires are more or less clear. They are confined to regions where the air temperature remains below $0°C$ for more than 200 days of the year and where precipitation between November and April is less than 300 mm (Lundquist[14]). This very roughly corresponds with the southern limit of the discontinuous permafrost, and it is interesting to note that in both Finland and Canada the permafrost makes its first appearance within the palsa mounds and other elevated surface features of the mire.

It is thus clear that the peat must act as an insulating blanket which helps to prevent the thawing of the ground ice, producing the nuclei of the hidden ice masses. The surface peats do thaw each summer, producing an active layer charged with melt water which allows the continual growth of the mire system. During the winter the whole surface will be frozen thus preventing water loss by evapotranspiration.

Brown[15] gives the following account of the possible mechanism of palsa formation. Initially these features appear as low mounds, or upwarpings, of peat protruding above the water level in the middle of shallow ponds. The mechanism of their formation and control of their distribution is uncertain, but it is suggested that the ponds freeze to the bottom in winter and the underlying saturated peat is domed up at random locations by intensive frost action and ice lens growth. When elevated above the pond level, the dry layer of exposed peat insulates the underlying frozen mass from summer thawing, this marking the initiation of a perennially frozen or permafrost condition. The

27

elevation of the peat surface above the ground level of the surrounding flat surface exposes it to winter winds which reduce or remove snow cover. Winter frost penetration is therefore greater than in the surrounding low, flat areas, which contributes to further permafrost accumulation.

As the peat continues to accumulate year after year accompanied by the increase in permafrost thickness each winter, the mounds grow and coalesce to form ridges and plateaux. Old age and degradation set in when the insulating ground cover ruptures due to biological oxidation and general deterioration, and thawing penetrates into the underlying frozen core.

Figure 2.10 gives details of a large palsa mound from western Lapland.

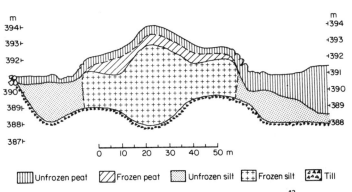

Figure 2.10. Profile of a large palsa mound (Redrawn after Salmi[43])

It is interesting to note, see Figure 2.2, that the distribution of the Fennoscandian palsamires is inland, indicating that the influence of the arctic ocean ameliorates the climate enough to preclude their development in the coastal areas.

Passing westwards from zone 5 the influence of the Atlantic ocean, especially where affected by the warm Gulf stream, makes its influence felt on the mire development in another way.

Zone 7b Ridge raised mires. This is the most difficult zone to delimit. Ridge raised mires were first described from the Pripet Marshes by Kulczynski[16], they have since been described from Poland, Bitner[17] and montane Bavaria, Bellamy[18]. They lie intermediate between the domed mires of zone 5 and the blanket mires of zone 8. They are found in climatic regions where tertiary peat growth can carry the peat reservoir over low water partings to coalesce with the mire systems developing in

28

adjacent basins. The example shown in Figure 2.11 is a type specimen described by Kulczynski, those of the main zone have cupolas which may exceed 5 m in height.

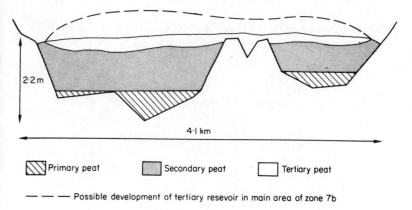

Figure 2.11. Profile of a ridge raised mire. The height of the component cupolas depends in part on the area of the mire and in part on the climate of the area

Zone 8b Blanket mires. Along the northwestern seaboard of Europe and on the mountains of Scotland, Northern England, Wales and Ireland peat can develop directly on the mineral ground up to a considerable angle of slope. Tansley[19] sets the limits at about 10°, Taylor[20] at about 18° but in the mountains of Western Ireland peat layers more than 2 m deep are present on slopes of 25°. Where favourable topography exists blanket mires live up to their name, covering vast tracts of land. Blanket mire is simply a further development from the ridge raised mire in response to the wet humid Atlantic climate.

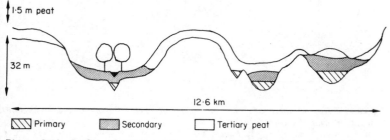

Figure 2.12. Profile of blanket mire showing all the component mire types

The example shown in Figure 2.12 is a hypothetical case, a collage showing all the main types of mire which can be found within the blanket mire complex.

Zone 9. Arctic mires dependent upon the presence of continuous permafrost (see pages 32 and 41).

The range of mire complex types found in Europe is summarised in Figure 2.13 together with the climatic types which typify each zone.

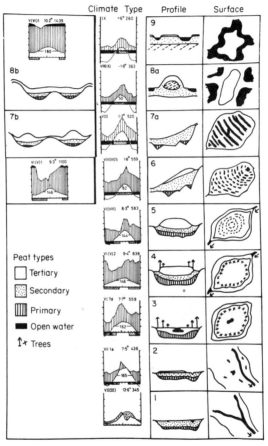

Figure 2.13. Summary of the main types of mire complex found in Europe, together with the climate diagrams which typify each zone. For an explanation of the climate diagrams, see Figure 2.5. The roman numerals indicate the climate types (Walters and Lieth[6])

30

ZONATION AND THE BOREAL MIRES OF NORTH AMERICA

Study of the European situation indicates that extensive tertiary peat development is confined to areas of high incidence and amount of rainfall. Only the palsamires are found in areas with less than 400 mm of rain per annum.

The peatland (Muskeg) map of Canada (Radforth[21]) on the other hand shows the main area of extensive peat development to be in the tundra and subarctic regions, much of which receives less than 400 mm per annum. It is even more surprising when it is realised that much of the peatlands of Canada appear to be of the blanket mire type, covering whole landscapes. The term 'unconfined' (Radforth[22]) is used to distinguish them from the confined (Primary) mires which are found further south.

In the Atlantic climate of Newfoundland with a rainfall in excess of 1000 mm, true blanket mires have been described by Pollett[23].

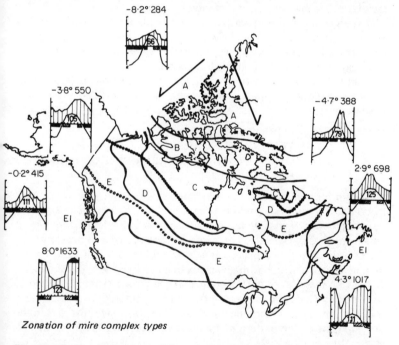

Zonation of mire complex types

Figure 2.14. The probable zonation of the types of mire complex found in Canada. Climatic diagrams from sites within each zone are also shown. The solid dotted line delineates the southern limit of the continuous permafrost, and the open dotted line delineates the southern limit of the discontinuous permafrost

31

Figure 2.14 also shows the approximate limits of the permafrost and the discontinuous permafrost and it is suggested that the perennially frozen ground offers sufficient explanation for the existence of these extensive areas of tertiary peat in the semiarid continental climate.

For much of the year, the soil and its overlying peat is frozen to the surface and the peat forming plant communities and any decomposers present spend the majority of the year in a dormant state. At the onset of the growing season the frost begins to melt from the surface downwards producing an active layer charged with melt water. It is important also to note that the bulk of the annual precipitation occurs during the summer months keeping the ecosystem supplied with water. The plant communities undergo very rapid development netting as much as 5 g/m^2 /day, some of which is laid down as peat. It is during this period that the bulk of the decomposition takes place and the peat becomes charged with CO_2. This is released slowly by diffusion but the main period of release is during the refreeze at the onset of winter.

The importance of the peat as an insulating blanket (Brown[24]) cutting down the depth of summer thaw (see page 27) is emphasised and the term 'thermal blanket mire' suggests itself as a general term for the unconfined muskegs of the Canadian subarctic.

Study of the airform pattern of the mires as seen from 10000 ft indicates the following zonation within the 'thermal blanket mire' zone (Radforth[25]) which are also shown in Figure 2.14.

A and B   EMBRYO MIRES
C   TERRAZZOID MARBLOID
D   MARBLOID WITH RETICULOID INTRUSIONS
E   RECTICULOID MARBLOID

Within the area of continuous permafrost the pattern terrazzoid with marbloid interruption predominates, Plate 2.4. Study on the ground reveals a matrix of shallow lakes, pools and flark-like depressions within which small raised terraces are found in various stages of development. These have been called palsa plateaux and Brown's scheme for the formation of palsas includes the plateaux as an early stage in development. It must be made clear at this point that the 'Brown' formation scheme does not preclude the idea put forward by Koppijaako and Radforth[26] that pattern in the underlying mineral terrain may play some part in the development of the pattern of the mire surface. This is further investigated on pages 41 and 42.

As the palsa plateaux develop they grow out to form the lobed interdigitating masses which produce the marbloid airform pattern which is dominant across the zone of discontinuous permafrost, Plate 2.5. One

Plate 2.4.   Terrazoid airform pattern from 300m altitude. The whole terrain is covered in peat, the most outstanding features being the raised islands ringed with trees, which are developing palsa plateaux. Note the white colouration which is due to an abundance of lichens in their centres. Photograph is of an area near Fort Churchill, Manitoba, Canada.

fact must be borne in mind, that is that in these high latitudes peat growth will be very slow and patterns once present will persist, especially bearing in mind the persistence of frost in any raised areas which will help to accentuate such patterns.

Passing southwards, the increasing period of development of the living landscape since the melting of the ice must also be remembered. Thus at least part of the zonation could be simply related to the time since biotic development was possible in the periglacial fringe.

South of the discontinuous permafrost three extensive areas covered

Plate 2.5. Marbloid airform pattern from 300m altitude. The palsa plateaux dominated by thick mats of lichens (see Plate 2.4) have grown out and coalesced to form the great lobed masses which will in time cover the terrain separated only by the main drainage axes. Photograph is of an area near Fort Churchill, Manitoba, Canada.

with muskeg have been described in the literature; the Hudson Bay Lowlands (Sjörs[27]), the Lake Agassiz region of Minnesota, U.S.A., (Heinselman[28]) and the mires of the Laurentian Shield near Georgian Bay (Radforth[29]).

The first two areas include large expanses of 'patterned fen' and string bogs' which greatly resemble the aapamire of Fennoscandia. Heinselman's definitions given below indicate that close relationships exist between the three.

34

String bogs, Strangmoore; Circumboreal class of patterned bogs having more or less parallel bog ridges, separated by wet (often sedgy) hollows. In some regions the ridges join to form nets. Ridges lie across the slope, at right angles to water movement.

Patterned Fen; A fen-like area having alternate more or less parallel, peat ridges and hollows orientated across the slope, i.e. at right angles to water movement (closely allied with strangemoore or string bog).

There seems little or no doubt that string bogs, patterned fens and aapamires are basically the same type of mire complex and they will be considered as such. All exhibit a reticuloid airform pattern.

Sjörs[27] also describes mires which greatly resemble the excentric mire complexes already described from Finland. 'On the south side of the Attawapiskat (river) we observed some bogs that slope unilaterally towards the river, but with some divergent directions of slope as seen from the fan-like arrangmeent of the hollows and bog pools'.

He also describes various types of domed mire from the area, including a unique type which occurs in the form of a hogsback-like dome up to 3 m high formed on the ridges between adjacent rivers and streams. These may be over 20 km long and less than 2 km wide.

One striking feature of the mires of the Hudson Bay Lowland area is the abundance of mounds each of which is usually covered with dense stands of black spruce (*Picea mariana*). Sjörs describes two types, oval and teardrop, the latter with 'tails' pointing in the direction of flow of the water. Porsild, reported by Sjörs[27], states 'the origin of these spruce islands is not clear, it would seem likely however that they developed during a period with a colder climate. In many spruce "islands" the centre has collapsed so that they now appear ring shaped. The rim is forested and the centre a treeless wet mire. Often a shallow moat-like depression circles the "island". The ring shaped black spruce "island" is clearly the result of collapse, or thawing out, of its former permafrost core. The rim, which still contains remnants of a permafrost core, is often fractured or broken up into irregularly shaped blocks by deeply eroded fissures, the moat is almost certainly caused by the settling of the rim into the soft, no longer frozen, mineral sub-soil.'

The 'spruce islands' therefore represent a more southerly variety of palsa mound, developed in a climate which allows the growth of trees on the better drained elevated peats. The role of the tree canopy, which acts as an 'umbrella' preventing an insulating blanket of snow from building up on the peat surface, must also aid frost penetration.

The occurrence of many of the mire complex types together in one area would lend weight to topographic rather than, or as well as, climatic control of the development of these main mire types. However, as stated above, the zonation is far from clearcut even in Europe, and much more basic survey is needed in the vast area of Canada before the broad zonation (as described for Europe), even if it exists, becomes clear.

Heinselman[28] describes patterned mires, aapamire, from further south in Minnesota. Here, although the aapamires are not the dominant form of mire complex, he states that, once the pattern features are recognised, it becomes apparent that nearly all of the mires in the region exhibit patterning to some degree.

Black spruce islands which are usually large, that is more than 8 km long, and small tamarak islands are abundant in the area. All those investigated by Heinselman were developed over underlying peat deposits showing that they did not begin their growth until well after peat formation began in the area. He states that a satisfactory explanation for the origin and location of these islands has not been found. He rules out several possibilities, substrate, topography and the fact that they may be genetically related to those described from the Hudson Bay Lowlands. There is no evidence from structural studies nor from palynology (Fries[30]) that they represent palsa mounds developed in an earlier colder climatic period. Everything points to the fact that they are profile developments which must be accounted for by processes that are operating today. This must of course be equally true for the other surface patterns, the strings and the flarks, this will be discussed further below. However, there is one point of great interest before leaving the spruce islands, which is that similar structures are found in the primary

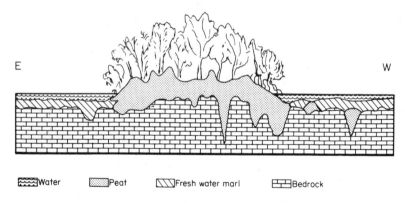

E   W

▨ Water   ▦ Peat   ◩ Fresh water marl   ▤ Bedrock

Figure 2.15. Profile of a hammock dominated by hardwoods interspersed with Paurotis palms (Redrawn after Spackmann et al[3])

mire systems of the Everglades far to the south in Florida (Spackman *et al*[3]). These are the famous hammocks or tree islands of the Everglades and they can be either elliptical, round or teardrop in plan, the main colonising tree being the cypress, *Taxodium distichum,* followed by hardwoods. Figure 2.15 shows a section through a typical hammock, however they are not all formed over elevations of the bed rock. Their existence appears to depend on the presence of the swamp cypress which can grow in the shallow water thus diverting the main flow of ground water allowing peat to accumulate. What is not at all clear is what limits the size of the hammocks. Whatever the answers to the problems are it seems that wherever mires are formed on gentle slopes, and trees can grow, raised islands of peat associated with trees will form. This association with trees is of great interest. All higher plants contain lignin, those which are secondarily thickened, especially trees, contain enormous amounts. The lignin molecule includes in its make up phenol rings and is very resistent to decay. Lignin is in fact an important 'preservative'. The importance of lignin and lignin-like compounds in the genesis of coal and peat merits much more investigation.

PATTERNING OF THE BOREAL MIRES

The whole problem of the development of the surface features of the patterned boreal mires has been the field of much speculation but for obvious reasons, little actual experiment.

The earliest attempt at any explanation was the hummock-hollow regeneration complex theory put forward by Sernander and Von Post[31]. The surface of domed mires, especially in the Baltic region, consists of a mosaic pattern of hummocks and hollows. The development of this pattern is biotic in origin, simply a reflection of the fact that certain species of the bog moss Sphagnum can grow in the form of hummocks while other more hydrophilic species can only exist in pools of water. The postulated growth mechanism is simply that hummocks and hollows replace each other in a cyclical manner as the water table is carried upwards by capillarity.

Stratigraphical evidence supporting this theory is confusing, as some investigators find an alternation of hummock and hollow phases in the peat profile, (Kulczynski[16], Tolonen[13]), thus pointing to cyclical regeneration. Others find both hummock phase and hollow phase peats running continuously down through the profile (Walker and Walker[32], Aarolath[33]).

Kulczynski's proposed mechanism for the growth of continental domed mires which is shown in Figure 2.16 provides a logical explanation for both types of stratigraphy. The growth of the cupola is simply a

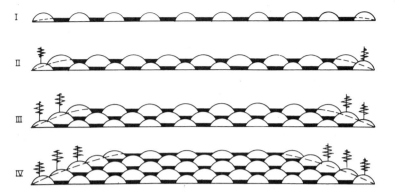

Figure 2.16. Diagram of one possible scheme of lenticular regeneration of peat. The black shading denotes regeneration hollows (Sphagnum cuspidatum), *the white regeneration hummocks* (Sphagnum fuscum). *The broken line denotes the water table in the peat, rising as regeneration proceeds (Redrawn after Kulczynski[16])*

process of vertical extension of the secondary peat reservoir. Whether the rising water table is due to internal factors such as the increase in capillary mass or from external factors such as general rise of the regional or local water table does not really matter. The hummocks and hollows are biotic phenomena and can be present from the initiation of peat growth. If the rise in water table is gradual and continuous then the persistence of the two phases throughout the profile is easily understood. If the gradual rise of water is halted for any period (or periods) of time allowing drying out of the hummock phase and subsequent colonisation by lichens and thus cessation of hummock growth, a profile of alternating hummock and hollow phases could easily result. It is interesting that in some profiles the hollow phase is entirely missing and the profile consists of alternating layers of highly humified peat streaks rich in lichens and slightly humified Sphagnum peat (Tolonen[34]) again pointing to periods of stabilisation of the rising water table.

The alignment of the hummocks and hollows in relation to the main slopes of the peat cupola is more difficult to contain within a single hypothesis.

The zonation described for the montane domed mire on page 18 perhaps gives some clue to an explanation. On the Wurzacher Ried the apex of the cupola consists of an almost featureless lawn of Sphagnum resembling a gigantic hollow, the water table being at or above the actual peat surface in all but the driest periods. Arranged around this are zones dominated by other species of Sphagna, especially those like *Sphagnum fuscum* which form large hummocks. It is onto these hummocks that trees (*Pinus mugo*) make their first appearance, the outer two zones being pioneer and mature pine forest, the latter situated on the more steeply shelving edges of the cupola (the rand). In successive zones the slope of the peat surface is more pronounced and the average depth of peat surface to the water table increases. The concentric arrangement is thus a result of growth mechanism and the slope of the cupola and its effect on the ground water levels. It is suggested that similar factors could account for the concentric patterns of hummocks and hollows found on treeless domed mires further north.

The much more pronounced surface features, such as the strings and flarks found in higher latitudes and their arrangement at right angles to the main direction of slope is of great interest and there are numerous theories to account for them. These can be conveniently divided into biotic, frost and ice action and gravity.

Biotic

A basic hummocky topography can simply be the result as stated above of the growth habit of certain of the mire plants, and this could be the basis for all the patterns described in the literature.

Once such a basic pattern has been initiated it could be accentuated as follows. The alternation of dry and wet periods has been used to explain the peculiar microstratigraphy found in many peat deposits (see page 153). Drying of the mire surface due to drought will have much more drastic effects on the more hygrophilous communities of the hollows, than on the more adaptable hummocks formers. The species in the hollows will die and deep cracks will develop in the peat leading to further rapid water loss by drainage.

Revitalisation of peat growth often leaves the hollows devoid of vegetation, producing shallow pools with black 'mud bottoms' (Sjörs[27]). The first plants to colonise the mud bottoms are algae such as *Zygogonium ericetorum* which can rapidly develop to produce a thin mat which covers the basal peat, The algal mat not only presents a barrier to colonisation by other plants and especially to the germination of seeds but also helps to arrest peat growth in another way. High rates of oxygen evolution from the photosynthesising algal film rapidly saturate the shallow water. This is particularly the case at low temperatures at which oxygen dissolves more readily in water. The resulting high dissolved oxygen concentrations promote corrosive oxidation which retard and impede the accumulation of peat.

One other factor which must be of importance is that very few higher plants and usually no woody plants with their high lignin content grow in the pools. Lundquist[35] has made a detailed study of flark formation and has shown that for periods in excess of 2000 years no organic matter, not even pollen grains which are highly resistant to decay, has accumulated in the depressions. This points to an extremely efficient process of corrosive oxidation probably much of which is due to microorganisms. Sjörs[36] points out that these conditions are more prevalent in the main boreal and subarctic regions than in the climatically more favoured zones.

Ice and Frost Action

There is much evidence that ice and frost action can cause uplift thereby creating a hummocky topography, see page 4. In the same way ice action could work within a biologically determined hummock-hollow system, intensifying the pattern. However the persistence of those features and the contemporary development of them in actively growing peat masses far south of the permafrost region would point to some other or at least some parallel explanation for the phenomena. Certainly the ordered alignment of the pools and hummocks and the flarks and the strings could be in part due to the formation of regular pressure ridges between the ice in the depressions, which thaws more rapidly than in strings which persists for a great length of time. Such a pattern once set up would probably be maintained for a very long period of time due to the slow growth of peat in these high latitudes.

Gravity

All the patterned mires have one feature in common, they are all formed on very gentle slopes or develop their own sloping surface due to peat growth. 'A prerequisite of their existence is an extraordinarily smooth topography with long regular and very slight slopes' (Sjörs[27]). It is therefore suggested that these patterns may simply be the result of gravity acting downslope on the basic biotic patterning discussed above. Troll[37] suggested that the patterning was caused by the tendency of the peat to glide downhill. Some support is given to this by the work of Pearsall[38] where he likened the developing section of blanket mire to a drop of semiliquid peat tending to flow downhill. He described the surface patterning of the mire as a series of split pools and pressure ridges. Such split pools, often crescentric in pattern, are a feature of certain types of blanket mire in Scotland.

The following observations on Muckle Moss in Northern England lend some weight to the gravity sliding hypothesis. Muckle Moss is a mire which fills the head of a small valley. On two occasions, forest fences have been constructed across the mire and, in each case, they have, over the course of years, bowed and eventually fractured; the bowing being due to the peat mass gradually sliding downslope. The rate of movement in the centre of the mire (where the movement is greatest) is about 5 cm per annum. The only other surface features of the mire are large, deep, steep sided crescentic pools, see Figure 2.17, running from the edge towards the centre of the peat mass. There is little doubt that these are splits caused by the tearing related to the gradual movement of the peat downslope. It is interesting to note that many of the mires in the region are known by the local name of 'flows' and there are many authentic accounts of catastrophic peat slides, bog bursts and bog flows whence these particular types of mire get their local name.

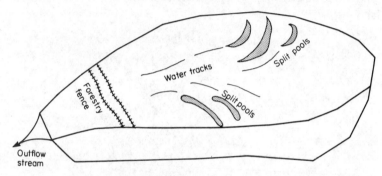

Figure 2.17. Diagrammatic representation of Muckle Moss, a valley head mire, the peat mass of which is gradually sliding down the slope

There probably is no single explanation and all the mechanisms considered above probably play some part in the process on some sites. The longevity of the features once initiated would appear to be a fruitful area for study.

THE INITIATION OF PEAT AND THE UNDERLYING PATTERN

North of the thermal blanket mire zone of Central Canada, muskeg is found as far north as mineral substrata exist without an overburden of permanent ice. The young periglacial landscapes of the arctic islands are patterned by ice and frost action. Wherever sortable deposits are found ordered patterns of sorted stripes, raised circles, ice wedge polygons etc., are a dominant feature of the terrain. Washburn[39] gives an account of the plethora of patterns and of theories relating to their development.

The important fact is that peat growth, (mire formation) is initiated in the lower, wetter places within these basic patterns, e.g. between the

41

sorted circles and polygons and in the stripe depressions. These places are more sheltered from adverse climatic effects such as high winds, and therefore collect an insulating deposit of snow, which decreases frost penetration. Thawing begins in these depressions which receive melt waters from the active layer which develops later in the more elevated portions of the patterns. The embryo mires are thus primary mires developing in the microdrainage axes, see Plate 2.7. From these beginnings the peat grows up to cover the whole underlying pattern, gradually obscuring them as the terrazoid and marbloid airform patterns develop (Koppijaako and Radforth[26]). However, far to the south well into the main marbloid zone, the position of the underlying skeleton of polygons and slope stripes may still be seen from the air although they are

(a)

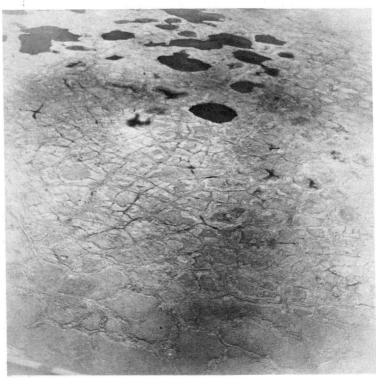

Plate 2.6. The 'Periglacial' landscape on Herschel Island, Yukon Territories, Canada. (a) was taken from an altitude of 300m and shows an extensive pattern of

42

invisible on the ground. This development is a function of the time since the terrain was first freed from ice and/or the situation of the terrain within the main drainage axes. Study of early peat development along a transect passing from the Arctic Islands south to the Boothia peninsula (Bellamy *et al*[40]) indicates that the rapidity of the development of extensive peatlands is related to the position of the site within the main drainage axes roughly in the following order: coastal deltas, river flood plains and open basins, closed basins, seepage area, watersheds. That is, the development of the mires takes place in what are hydrologically the most favourable sites.

Much more basic survey work is needed before these observations can be considered as anything more than tenuous hypotheses.

(b)

ice wedged polygons. The embryo mire vegetation is developing in the depressions between the polygons. (b) is a close up of one of the corners of a polygon

ZONATION OF THE PAN BOREAL MIRES

Extensive survey is also necessary to formalise the overall zonation described above for North America. Sellmann[41] working in Alaska indicates that the same zones are found right across the northern part of the continent, especially those mire types which have characteristics related to perennially frozen ground. The zones between the permanent ice caps and the southern limit of discontinuous permafrost appear in part related to a genetic series determined by the time taken for the peat blanket to grow, obscuring the ground surface features and developing the features which give the typical northern muskeg airform patterns.

South of this the aapamires with their palsas of the Hudson Bay Lowlands and those of Lake Aggasiz link the North American zonation to those described above for Europe. The European zones, together with those of United States which have at their southern limit the great primary deltaic mires of the Everglades are determined at least partly by macroclimatic factors.

The zonation is not perfect, other factors such as topography and altitude make their importance felt and produce mire complex types well outside their climatically typical zones.

Perhaps the best example described to date is that of an eccentric-concentric mire development at 700m in the Austrian Alps. Ullmann's[42] detailed investigation showed that its existence was due, at least in part, to the microclimate of the site, which lies in the shadow of a high mountain peak and receives no direct sunlight for two months each year.

Nevertheless the basic zonation does exist and the variation of the overall hydrological balance of mire sites, across and within the zonation, adequately contains and explains the range of variation of mire complexes found in the Northern hemisphere.

REFERENCES

1. CHEBOTAREV, A.A. *Theory of stream runoff.* Translated (1966) Israel Programme. Oldbourne 463 (1962).
2. DAVIS, J.H. 'The natural features of Southern Florida, especially the vegetation of the Everglades.' *Florida Geol. Survey Bull.* **25**, 311 (1943).
3. SPACKMAN, W., RIEGEL, W.L. and DOLSEN, C.P. 'Geological and Biological Interactions of the Swamp-Marsh Complex of Southern Florida. *Geol. Soc. America Inc. Special Paper.* 144, 35 (1968).
4. GRAND 'EUREY, C. *Carbonifere du Department de la Loire.* Parish Imprimerie Nationale (1877).
5. ANDERSON, J. 'The flora of the peat swamp forest of Sarawak and Brunei.' *Gardens Bull. Singapore,* **20**, pt. 2 (1963).
6. WALTERS, H. and LIETH, H. KLIMADIAGRAMM-WELTATLAS JENA (1960).

7. BELLAMY, D.J. 'Depth, time scale in Ephemeral Swamp Ecosystems.' *Trop. Ecol.*, **8**, 67-73.
8. PLOT, R. *The Natural History of Staffordshire*, Oxford (1686).
9. GLOB, P.V. *The Bog People*, Paladin London, 142 (1971).
10. CAJANDER, A.K. 'Studien uber die Moore Finnlands.' *Acta Forest Fenn.* **2:3**, 1-140.
11. BERTSCH, K. *Sumpf und Moor als lebengemeinschaft.* Ravensburg Maier (1952).
12. RUUHIJARVI, R. 'Uber die Regionale Einteilung der Nordfinnischen Moore.' *Ann. Bot. Soc. Van:* **31**, 1-360 (1960).
13. TOLONEN, K. 'Uber die Entwicklung der Moore in Finnischen Nordkaralien.' *Ann. Bot. Fennici:* **4**, 1-146 (1967).
14. LUNDQUIST, A. 'Patterned Ground & Related Frost Phenomena. *Proc. 3rd Int. Peat Cong. Quebec,* 174-181 (1968).
15. BROWN, R.J.E. 'Occurrence of Permafrost in Canadian Peatlands.' *Proc. 3rd Int. Peat Cong. Quebec,* 174-181 (1968).
16. KULCZYNSKI, S. 'Peat bogs of Polesie.' *Mem. Acad. Cracovie.* **315**, 356 (1949)
17. BITNER, K. 'Torfowisko Wyzokie w Bagnowie.' *Przegl. Geogr.* **32**, 4 (1960).
18. BELLAMY, D.J. 'Ecological Studies on some European Mires.' *Ph.D. Thesis University of London* (2 vols), 620 (1967).
19. TANSLEY, A.G. *The British Islands and their Vegetation,* Cambridge, (1939).
20. TAYLOR, J.A. and TUCKER, R.B. 'The peat deposits of Wales, an inventory and interpretation. *Proc. 3rd Int. Peat Cong. Quebec,* 163-173 (1968).
21. RADFORTH, N.W. in MacFARLANE, *Muskeg Engineering Handbook,* Univ. Toronto Press, 298 (1969).
22. RADFORTH, N.W. 'Suggested Classification of Muskeg for the Engineer.' *Eng. Journ. (Canada),* **35**, No. 11, 1199-1210 (1952).
23. BROWN, R.J.E. Permafrost, Climafrost and The Muskeg. *Proc. 11th Muskeg Res. Conf.* N.R.C. Canada Res., Tech. Memo 87: 159-178 (1966).
24. POLLET, F.C. Classification of peatlands in Newfoundland. *Proc. 4th Int. Peat Cong. Helsinki.* **1**, 101-110 (1972).
25. RADFORTH, N.W. 'Organic Terrain organization from the air.' Handbook No. 2. *Defense Research Board Canada.* Report No. Rd 124 (1958).
26. KORPIJAAKKO, E.O. and RADFORTH, N.W. 'Development of Certain Patterned Ground in Muskeg as Interpreted from Aerial Photographs'. *Proc. 3rd Int. Peat Cong. Quebec,* 69-73 (1968).
27. SJORS, H. 'Bogs and Fens on Attawapiskat River Northern Ontario.' *Nat. Mus. Canada. Bull.* **186**, 133 (1961).
28. HEINSELMAN, M. 'Forest sites, bog processes and peatland types in the glacial Lake Agassiz region, Minnesota.' *Ecol. Monogr.* **33**, 4 (1963).
29. RADFORTH, N.W. 'Organic terrain and Geomorphology'. *Can. Geographer,* **71**, 8-11 (1962).
30. FRIES, M. 'Pollen profiles of late pleistocene and recent sediments from Weber Lake, northeastern Minnesota'. *Ecology* **43**, 295-308 (1962).
31. VON POST, L. and SERNANDER, R. 'Pflanzen-Physiognomische Studien auf Torfmooren in Närke.' *Livretguide des Excursions en Suede du XI Cong. Geol. Inst.* 1-14 (1910).
32. WALKER, D. and WALKER, P.M. 'Stratigraphic evidence of regeneration in some Irish Bogs.' *J. Ecol.* **49**, 169-185 (1961).
33. AARTOLAHTI, T. 'Oberflachenformen von Hochmooren und Ihre Entwicklung in Südwest-Häme und Nord-Satakunta.' *Fennia* **93**, pt. 1, 1-268 (1965).

45

34. TOLONEN, K. 'On the regeneration of North European bogs 1.' *Acta. Agr. Fenn.* **123**, 143-166 (1971).
35. LUNDQUIST, A. 'Beskrivning till Jordartskarta over Kapparbergs lan.' *Sverives Geol. Unders.* **21**, 1-213 (1951).
36. SJÖRS, H. 'The mire vegetation on Upper Langan District in Jämtland.' *Ark. Bot. Uppsala.* **33** No. 6, 1-96 (1946).
37. TROLL, C. 'Structure, soils, solifluxion and frost climates of the earth.' *Geol. Rundschav* **34**, 545-694 (1944)
38. PEARSALL, W.H. 'Two blanket bogs in Sutherland.' *J. Ecol.* **44**, 493-516 (1966).
39. WASHBURN, A.L. 'Classification of Patterned Ground and review of suggested origins.' *Bull. Geol. Soc. Amer.* **67**, 823-866 (1966).
40. BELLAMY, D.J. and RADFORTH, N.W. A pattern of muskeg (In Press, 1973).
41. SELLMANN, P.V. 'Properties and Destruction of two characteristic Peat Environments in Alaska.' *Proc. 3rd Int. Peat Cong. Quebec.* 157-163 (1968).
42. ULLMANN, H. and STEHLIK, A. 'A moss of nordic type in the Alps.' *Proc. 4th Int. Peat Cong. Helsinki.* **1**, 75-89 (1972).
43. SALMI, M. 'Development of Palsas in Finnish Lapland. *Proc. 3rd Int. Peat Cong. Quebec,* 182-190 (1968)

Chapter Three

The Geochemical Template

The oceans are the source of the global circulation of water and the sink for the products of global erosion whether geochemical or biogeochemical. The chemical composition and concentration of 'average' oceanic water is given in Table 3.1, and must be regarded partly as a function of the abundance of the various minerals in the surface of the crust, their solubility and geological time, and addition from volcanic action.

The freshwaters of the world are agents in the process of erosion and vehicles for the transport of the products of erosion. Clarke[1] was the first to show that four cations, calcium, (Ca^{++}), magnesium (Mg^{++}), sodium (Na^+) and potassium (K^+) and the three anions, bicarbonate (HCO_3^-), sulphate (SO_4^{--}) and chloride (Cl^-) account for all but a small fraction of the total ionic concentration of freshwaters, these being termed the major ions by Rodhe.[2] The average composition, of the freshwaters of the world, recalculated after Clarke[1] and Conway[3] by Gorham[4] is given in Table 3.2. The early analytical data led to the concept of 'an average freshwater' as a standard whose ionic proportions would be gradually approached by all water through the operation of ionic exchange processes between water and the soils and rocks through which they percolate, if sufficient time were allowed (Rodhe[2]).

TABLE 3.1
AVERAGE CONCENTRATION OF
CERTAIN IONS IN SEA WATER

Ion	p.p.m.
Na^+	1070
Mg^{++}	130
Ca^{++}	40
K^+	40
Cl'	1930
SO_4''	270
HCO_3'	10

TABLE 3.2
IONIC COMPOSITION OF THE AVER-
AGE FRESHWATER OF THE WORLD
(MODIFIED FROM GORHAM 1961)

Ion	p.p.m.
Ca^+	15·0
Mg^{++}	2·4
Ca^{++}	8·7
K^+	1·0
HCO_3'	53·0
SO_4''	18·1
Cl'	8·3

Total ionic concentration
2·35 m equiv./litre

The enormous variation in the ionic composition of freshwater on a local, let alone a global scale, points to the fact that even if such a hypothesis is tenable,(Hutchinson[5]), the operative 'sufficient time' has not yet elapsed. The marked difference in the dominance of monovalent cations in the 'standard' sea water over the dominance of the divalent cations in 'standard' freshwater alone shows that on a world scale a significant proportion of the mobilisable Na and K has already been moved from the catchment to the sea.

The complex of factors affecting the contemporary chemistry of freshwaters are listed below:

1. The chemical composition of the rain falling on the catchment.
2. The geology of the catchment, especially of all surface and sub-surface routes of water transport, these will be collectively called 'aquifers' throughout this chapter.
3. The topography of the catchment and its drainage systems.
4. Climate, affecting both the rates of weathering and hence the availability of minerals, and the concentration and dilution of the resultant water body.
5. Biotic, modification brought about by biogeochemical cycles.
6. Time, the time that the aquifers have been exposed to leaching, and the rate of water movement through the aquifers.

CHEMICAL COMPOSITION OF THE RAINWATER

The bulk of the water in circulation in the atmosphere is derived from the sea by evaporation. This water, which amounts to only about 0.06% of the total global water, that is, 875×10^{12} litres, can pick up chemicals in a number of ways. Woodcock[6] suggests the following mechanism of entrainment of minerals from the ocean. High winds lead to the breaking of waves at sea producing foam patches containing a multitude of small bubbles. When the bubbles burst at the surface, they shoot up tiny jets which break into droplets at their tips. Many of the droplets are sufficiently small to be swept up into the air and may evaporate there to form salt particles which are capable of acting as nuclei for cloud and raindrop condensation or of being captured by raindrops. Minerals taken into the atmosphere in this way will be carried by the water vapour masses until deposited in the rain. Supply of such minerals to any terrain will be dependent on its distance from the sea, the amount of rainfall and the incidence of stormy weather with onshore winds. The importance of this source of minerals is indicated by the study of Mackereth and Heron[7], which showed that a two day westerly gale raised the concentration of sodium in Ennerdale Water by 0.7 p.p.m. The lake is situated 12 km from the coast at an altitude of 160 m and yet about 3 000 t of sea water must have been deposited on the drainage basin in that time in order to bring about this change. Junge[8] has demonstrated for onshore winds a linear relationship between the sea salt concentration of atmospheric aerosols and wind force on the Beaufort scale.

TABLE 3.3
AVERAGE IONIC CONCENTRATION OF 1 YEAR'S PRECIPITATION IN p.p.m. (MODIFIED FROM GORHAM, 1961)

Collection Station	Ca +	Mg ++	Na +	K +	SO_4''	Cl'
Newfoundland	0·8	ND	5·2	0·3	2·2	8·9
Wisconsin	1·2	ND	0·5	0·2	2·9	0·2
Minnesota	1·0	ND	0·2	0·2	1·4	0·1
N. Sweden	1·2	0·2	0·4	0·3	2·5	0·7
Central Sweden	0·6	0·1	0·3	0·2	2·6	0·5
Georgetown Guyana	0·8	0·3	1·5	0·2	1·3	2·9

If this were the only source of minerals to the atmospheric water then the composition of rain, for which some data are given in Table 3.3, should approach that of sea water. The main source of modification would appear to be dust particles of terrestrial origin carried by the wind. Loess may be derived from the normal processes of erosion or from special geological activity such as that of volcanoes, the exact effect depending upon the type of parent material from which the loess was derived. The best evidence concerning the actual presence of loess in air masses comes from the rate of accumulation of dusts in snowfields lying under different wind systems, see Table 3.4, data from Windom[9].

TABLE 3.4
RATES OF ACCUMULATION OF DUSTS IN SNOWFIELDS LYING UNDER DIFFERENT WIND SYSTEMS. AFTER WINDOM (1969)

Wind System	Accumulation Rate $mm/10^3$ years
N Hemisphere polar easterlies	0·14
N Hemisphere westerlies	0·11-0·21
N Hemisphere trades	0·01-0·09
S Hemisphere polar easterlies	0·01

Two other important sources of minerals are organic particles, including pollen grains and spores, and the increasing influence of atmospheric 'pollution' especially supplying sulphate. Regarding the latter there is some evidence that hydrogen sulphide (H_2S) from the bottom muds of the continental shelf, especially from estuaries, released to the atmosphere could be oxidised to sulphate thus increasing the concentration of this anion in the rain.

49

Particles held in suspension in the air streams will be washed out by the rain and there is evidence that light rain is more concentrated than heavy rainfall, the operative factor being the dilution volume in relation to the washout of atmospheric mineral load. It is thus obvious that there will be a pattern of the chemical composition and concentration of rainwater depending on where it falls and how it falls.

Once rain has fallen on the surface of the earth and has become surface or ground water further modifications of its dissolved chemical load will take place. Composition will mainly be affected by the geology of the catchment and its aquifers, concentration by the climate, especially the balance between precipitation and evaporation.

SURFACE AND SUBSURFACE GEOLOGY

Gorham[4] states 'it must be emphasised that soil and rock weathering provides the major supply of ions to natural water'. Some data which show the effect of surface geology on the chemical composition of fresh water are given in Table 3.5. The effects are not however related only to the absolute composition of the rocks but also to the degree of mineralisation which in part must control the supply through availability. The actual physical structure of the deposit will also be of importance, controlling the rate of percolation and hence the time course of solution. The importance of chemical weathering producing clay minerals with large exchange capacities, Jenny[10], must control in part the loss to gravitational water and the equilibrium state of the developing and mature soils.

Springwater discharging from underground aquifers will often have very different chemical composition from that of the immediate area into which it discharges. In extreme cases where the discharge volume is very great the chemical composition and indeed even the temperature of the discharging water may vary very little over long periods of time, thus providing what are virtually chemostable and thermostable conditions for field experiments, see Odum et al[11].

CLIMATE

All climatic factors play a direct role in both the processes of mechanical and chemical weathering. It is, however, the balance between precipitation and evaporation which has the main effect upon the concentration of the solutes. In this respect, size, depth and type of basin will also be of importance. The water in closed basins (seepage lakes) will be more susceptible to the effects of evaporation and dilution than those of open basins. However, closed basins which derive their main supply from surface runoff will receive only meagre supplies of

TABLE 3.5
DATA COMPARING THE COMPOSITION OF WATERS DRAINING VARIOUS GEOLOGICAL SUBSTRATA (p.p.m.)
AFTER GORHAM (1961)

Drainage	Total Cations m. equiv./litre	pH	Ca	Mg	Na	K	HCO_3	SO_4	Cl
Nova Scotian									
Granite	0·35	4·7	1·0	0·5	5·2	0·4	NIL	5·9	7·7
Quartzite and Slate	0·29	5·7	2·1	0·4	3·0	0·6	1·8	5·2	4·9
Carboniferous Strata	0·37	6·5	3·0	0·6	3·6	0·5	6·1	5·3	5·4
Bohemian									
Phyllite	NR	NR	5·7	2·4	5·4	2·1	35·1	3·1	4·9
Granite	NR	NR	7·7	2·3	6·9	3·7	40·3	9·2	4·2
Mica Schist	NR	NR	9·3	3·8	8·0	3·1	48·3	9·5	5·4
Basalt	NR	NR	68·8	19·8	21·3	11·0	326·7	27·2	5·7
Cretaceous Rocks	NR	NR	133·4	31·9	20·7	16·4	404·8	167·0	17·3

NR = No Record

TABLE 3.6
DATA COMPARING THE COMPOSITION OF THE WATERS OF DRAINAGE AND SEEPAGE LAKES

Sample	pH	Total Salts m. equiv./litre	H	Ca	Mg	Na	K	HCO$_3$	SO$_4$	Cl	SiO$_2$
Epping Forest											
Seepage Pond	NR	NR	NR	4·0	3·1	4·8	3·5	14·6	8·6	12·1	0·4
Drainage Pond	NR	NR	NR	45·4	33·2	24·2	4·7	119·0	144·0	44·4	8·0
Cheshire Meres & Lake District Rain											
Rain Water	4·5	0·17	0·02	0·2	0·1	1·0	0·1	NIL	1·7	1·8	NR
Water from Small Seepage Lake	3·9	0·55	0·07	0·9	0·4	2·7	0·6	NIL	6·5	4·9	NR
Water from Large Seepage Lake	4·7	1·05	0·01	3·8	1·3	4·5	·1·2	NIL	12·8	8·9	NR
Water from Seven Normal Drainage Lakes (Average)	8·0	4·53	NIL	24·5	7·3	8·9	2·1	66·3	35·9	14·2	NR

NR = No Record

minerals, whereas open basins (drainage lakes) are supplied by flowing ground water which has more chance of having passed through pervious aquifers and hence of picking up minerals in solution, see Table 3.6 (Gorham[12]).

The overall control will be the size of the lake in relation to its catchment and to its position within the drainage system of the landscape.

BIOTIC

Living organisms affect the composition and concentration of dissolved substances in three ways:

1. Modification by uptake and cycling of the biogeochemicals, that is mainly simple elements and compounds, and dissolved gases.
2. Modification of the exchangeable fraction of minerals held within the soil complex.
3. Addition of soluble organic chemicals, byproducts and excess of their metabolism.

Geochemicals and Biogeochemicals

Uptake of certain geochemicals into the biotic fraction of both animals and plants of the catchment ecosystems must bring about changes of the availability of these minerals to solution in ground water. The effect will be greatest in those minerals which are in short supply, such as potassium, nitrate and phosphate. Table 3.7 shows the relative amounts of key geochemicals in cycle in various types of 'climax' ecosystem. Periodicity in the growth of plant communities developing on catchments may therefore be reflected in a periodicity in the availability of certain minerals to the groundwaters. Nitrate is a special case in that its abundance in many waters will be determined by the activity of nitrogen fixing microorganisms. This aspect of mire ecology will be developed further in this chapter pages 75 to 77.

TABLE 3.7
AMOUNT OF GEOCHEMICALS HELD IN STANDING CROP OF VARIOUS
CLIMAX ECOSYSTEMS. DATA FROM RODIN AND BAZILEVICH (1970).

| | x 100 kilograms/hectare | | | |
	N	Ca	K	P
Tundra	80	20	15	13
Scrub Tundra	450	95	130	30
Coniferous Forest	680	480	340	85
Deciduous Forest	950	1340	560	90
Tropical Forest	2 900	2 680	1 800	320

The biological oxygen demand of any body of water which can render that water body, or any part of it, anaerobic can effect the mobilisation of certain minerals in the lake system. Mortimer[13] showed that under anaerobic conditions, sulphates were precipitated on the mud surface as ferrous sulphides; remobilisation only takes place in aerobic conditions.

Perhaps today the most active biotic factor effecting the mineral composition of the worlds fresh waters is man. Table 3.8 summarises some data comparing the amounts of elements mobilised into the atmosphere by the combustion of fossil fuels with those derived from weathering. Ground water enrichment is a common effect in areas where intensive modern agriculture is practised, the major effect being felt in sump areas, for example in some of the flat ill-drained areas of the American wheat belt, Walters[14]. The role of denitrification and of the modification of natural systems of nitrogen fixation have still to be investigated in detail. Suffice to say that the effects are still increasing and that the minerals in question are mainly those which are in short supply in the natural system. Where these are important nutrients such as K, N and P the term eutrophication is used, where they are toxicoids such as Pb, Cu and Hg the term pollution may be applied. Man is of course adding new chemicals (pesticides, herbicides, etc.) into the hydrosphere, but this is beyond the scope of this book.

TABLE 3.8
AMOUNTS OF SOME ELEMENTS MOBILISED INTO THE HYDROSPHERE AS A RESULT OF WEATHERING PROCESSES AND THE COMBUSTION OF FOSSIL FUELS. AFTER BERTINE AND GOLDBERG 1971

Element	Fossil Fuel mobilisation $x \cdot 10^9$ g/year Total	Weathering mobilisation $x \cdot 10^9$ g/year Total
Sodium	280	287 000
Magnesium	280	190 000
Potassium	> 140	131 000
Calcium	1 400	610 000
Phosphorus	> 70	> 720
Sulphur	3 400	>140 000
Mercury	1·6	3·5
Lead	3·6	131

The actual chemical composition and concentration of ground water solutes will depend on the complex of factors listed above. The permutations and combinations are enormous, thus accounting for the great variety of freshwaters found on earth, Clarke[1]. These are the chemical templates for the development of peat producing ecosystems.

54

The extreme case of Silver Springs, Florida (Odum *et al*[11]) in which the enormous and constant flow of water produces chemostatic and thermostatic conditions has already been mentioned. Flow, which is a function of volume and time, must be a major factor buffering against influences which could change the chemistry of any body of water. A key feature of the mire template is that flow must be reduced enough to allow the deposition of organic matter. It is thus obvious that one of the main biotic factors which will bring about changes in the chemistry of ground waters will be the process of peat formation itself.

MIRES AND THE CHEMISTRY OF MIRE WATERS

In all major treatises of mire classification and mire ecology, three basic types have been recognised, which are characterised as follows:

A	B	C	
Niedermoore	Ubergangsmoore	Hochmoore	(Weber[15])
Flachmoore	Zwischenmoore	Hochmoore	(Potonie[16])
Riekarr	Karr	Moss	(Melin[17])
Rich Fen	Poor Fen	Moss	(Sjörs[18])

Both Weber and Potonie make their distinction on the basis of ontogeny, identifying the stage of development from its initiation in a ground water (primary) reservoir, through to the stage of a tertiary reservoir fed only by rain water. This developmental sequence of mire types, Niedermoore to Ubergansmoore to Hochmoore was first proposed by Weber[19] in his terrestrialisation hypothesis.

The third classification is phytosociological, being based on floristic differences found between mires in the study area which was Fennoscandia. It in fact identifies differences but invokes no explanation. The summary of all the early analytical data of Swedish Lake waters by Kivinen[20] laid a firm foundation to the work of Witting[21, 22] and to the acceptance by Du Rietz[23] that the ground waters of the three mire types are chemically distinct. The differences separating the three groups were thus formalised in chemical terms. The 'mineral soil water limit' (Thunmark[24]) at about pH 4·0 and dissolved calcium at 1 mg/litre as the dividing line between groups B and C, and the 'calcareous water limit' (Witting[25]) at about pH 6·8 and dissolved calcium at 18 mg/litre separating groups A and B.

Sjörs[26], in his paper which discusses the relation between vegetation and electrolytes in North Swedish mire waters, raised the following doubts over the use of these strict ecological limits. 'There is above all one direction of variation which is very closely related to acidity and base content and that is that of the moss — poor fen — rich fen series. This series has been dealt with particularly by Du Rietz[28] and is regarded by him as the basis of subdivisions of the mire vegetation into main units. Du Rietz lays great stress on the boundaries between these units, 'I am more inclined to look upon this variation as gradual'. Sjörs recognises seven mire types on the basis of floristic makeup and, to a certain extent, habitat and shows that a broad correlation exists between the main direction of variation of the vegetation and the pH and conductivity of the surface waters of the mire. In essence he recognises the fact that any mire can be placed within the continuum of variation between the two extremes, both in terms of the floristic composition of its vegetation and the chemical composition of its ground waters.

In 1949 a fifth major treatise on mire ecology was published in which Kulczynski[29] proposed a terminology and a classification which link the ontogenic, phytosociologic and chemical approaches. He states: 'In Weber's hypothesis the developmental process of niedermoore to hochmoore is to be understood therefore as synonymous with the terrestrialisation process. The accrual of bog strata results in a regulated biotic succession. In consequence of the accrual of bog strata and of their moving away from the ground water level, an increasing deficiency of nutritive substances comes into evidence in the upper peat strata. Thereby conditions favourable for the invasion of the peat moss *Sphagnum* come into existence.'

Kulczynski goes on in his monograph to classify the mire systems which he studied into the following groups;

1. *Rheophilous* (cf. *niedermoore),* mires developing in mobile ground waters, the term means 'loving the flow'.

2. *Transition* (cf. *ubergangsmoore),* either rheophilous mires with an insufficient ground water supply, or mires which are in the process of change from a rheophilous to an ombrophilous water regime. The term simply infers intermediate in type or in the process of change.

3. *Ombrophilous* (cf. *hochmoore),* mires developing in immobile ground waters, their whole water supply coming from the rain falling directly on them, the term means 'loving the rain'.

Under ideal geomorphological and hydrological conditions the process would be a gradual change in water regime brought about by the accrual of peat, this is shown in Figure 3.1. Analysis of the model situation identifies the following stages in the process.

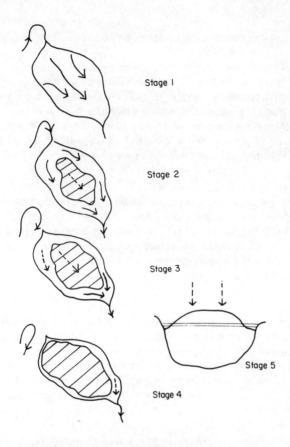

Figure 3.1. Model of the succession of mire types

The Model Situation

The water supply to the lake is of three types:—
1. Rain falling directly on the surface of the lake.
2. Runoff and seepage from the immediate catchment of the lake basin.
3. A continuous flow of a large enough volume of ground water to affect the whole lake, brought into the system by the inflow stream, from areas beyond the immediate catchment of the lake basin.

57

Stage 1

For the initiation of peat development in the flowing ground water, there are two possible phases:

1. With a large flow of water bringing much allochthonous material into the system, this, coupled with very slow rate of peat development in flowing oxygenated water, produces a very heavy peat. The water flow is thus directed above the peat.

2. Where the rate of water flow is less, less allochthonous material is brought into the system and a faster rate of growth produces a light peat. The water flow is thus directed below a floating mat.

Stage 2

The accrual of peat tends to canalise the main flow of water within the basin, leaving some areas (shown hatched in Figure 3.1), which are only subjected to the effects of mobile ground waters during periods of excessive inflow. Again, at least two phases may be recognised:

1. Where the whole peat mass is inundated.

2. Where the peat mass is not inundated.

Stage 3

Continued peat growth diverts the inflow from the basin; the water supply to the mire is thus restricted to rain falling directly on the mire surface runoff and influent seepage from the surrounding catchment. The bulk of the mire now is submitted only to an intermittent and much reduced water flow. Those regions lying in the main drainage tracts within the mire, however, may be subject to a slow continuous flow.

Stage 4

Further accrual of peat leaves large areas of the mire surface unaffected directly by moving water, but subject to inundation when the water level of the basin rises during periods of rainfall.

Stage 5

Because of continued peat growth the mire surface rises above the effect of the vertical oscillations of the ground water. The mire cupola so produced possesses its own water table fed by rain falling directly on it.

Bellamy[30], using the above as a model of succession in mire ecosystems, and drawing on hydrological, chemical and floristic data collected from 384 mires covering the European mire complex zones 4, 5, 6, 7B and 8B, hypothesises the existence of a cline of seven hydrological mire types bridging the two extremes.

Group A. Rheophilous

Mires under the influence of flowing ground waters derived from outside the immediate catchment of the mire, that is mires developing in drainage lakes. These mires typically have waters in which the predominant anion is bicarbonate and the predominant cation is calcium.

Hydrological Type 1. Continuously flowing waters which inundate the mire surface.

Hydrological Type 2. Continuously flowing water directed beneath a floating mat of vegetation.

Hydrological Type 3. Intermittent flow of water inundating the mire surface.

Hydrological Type 4. Intermittent flow of water directed beneath a floating mat of vegetation.

Group B. Transition

Mires under the influence of flowing ground water derived solely from the immediate catchment of the mire, that is, mires developing in seepage lakes. These mires typically have waters in which the predominant anion is sulphate and the predominant cation is calcium.

Hydrological Type 5. Continuous flow of water.

Hydrological Type 6. Intermittent flow of water.

Group C. Ombrophilous

Hydrological Type 7. Mires which are never subject to the influence of flowing ground water. These mires typically have waters in which the predominant anion is sulphate and the predominant cation is hydrogen.

Figure 3.2 and Table 3.9 summarise the relevant chemical data allowing comparison between the ionic makeup and concentration of the major ions in the mire waters. Absolute comparison between the two schemes is impossible owing to the different methods of study and of phytosociological and chemical analysis. However the overall ecological similarity of the two series and hence schemes of classification are obvious; a change from waters in which calcium and bicarbonate are the dominant ions to those dominated by the sulphate and hydrogen ions.

It is easy to understand how this change in water type could be brought about. All living organisms produce acid substances as byproducts of their oxidative metabolism. Acidic substances are by definition molecules or ions which have a tendency to lose a proton (Bronsted[31]). The hydrogen ions (protons) from any such substances produced by plants in flowing ground waters of rheophilous mires will

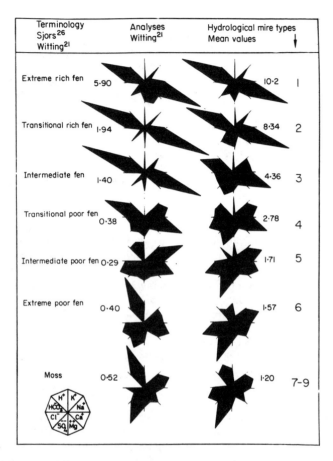

Figure 3.2. *Maucha diagrams comparing the mean composition of the major ions in waters of hydrological mire types 1-7 (Bellamy[30]) collected from most regions of Western Europe and the seven types of mire recognised in Scandanavia (Sjörs[18]). The area of the segments are proportional to the percentage equivalent concentration of the major cations and anions (see order in polygon). The figure beside each diagram is the total ionic concentration in milli equivalents per litre*

react with the bicarbonate present to form carbon dioxide and water and/or will be flushed away out of the system. Bicarbonate is the only relatively strong base (Bell[32]) found in abundance in natural waters (Clarke[1]). As peat begins to accumulate within the mire system, the effect of flowing ground water is gradually reduced and as the process continues the hydrogen ions will no longer be flushed away or neutralised

TABLE 3.9
MEAN VALUES OF THE CONCENTRATION OF MAJOR IONS IN WATERS FROM THE SEVEN HYDROLOGICAL MIRE TYPES (BELLAMY[30]) (DATA FROM WESTERN EUROPE, ALL REGIONS) AND THE SEVEN MIRE TYPES DESCRIBED FOR SCANDANAVIA (SJÖRS[26])

	pH	HCO_3	Cl	SO_4	Ca	Mg	Na	K	H	Total Major Ions
Hydrological Mire										
type 1	7·5	3·9	0·4	0·8	4·0	0·6	0·5	0·05	0	10·25
2	6·9	2·7	0·5	1·0	3·2	0·4	0·4	0·08	0	8·28
3	6·2	1·0	0·5	0·7	1·2	0·4	0·5	0·02	0	4·32
4	5·6	0·4	0·5	0·5	0·7	0·2	0·5	0·04	0·01	2·85
5	4·8	0·1	0·3	0·5	0·3	0·1	0·3	0·07	0·03	1·70
6	4·1	0	0·4	0·4	0·2	0·1	0·3	0·04	0·14	1·58
7	3·8	0	0·3	0·3	0·1	0·1	0·2	0·04	0·16	1·20
Sjörs types										
Extreme rich fen	7·7	2·3	0·2	0·4	1·8	0·9	0·2	0·02	—	5·9
Transitional fen	5·8	0·9	0·1	0·03	0·9	0·02	0·05	0·01	—	1·9
Intermediate fen	4·8	0·6	0·01	0·06	0·6	0·03	0·08	0·01	0·02	1·4
Transitional poor fen	5·5	0·1	0·04	0·04	0·1	0·03	0·06	—	—	0·38
Intermediate poor fen	4·4	0	0·03	0·05	0·06	0·03	0·08	—	0·4	0·29
Extreme poor fen	3·9	0	0·06	0·07	0·07	0·02	0·05	—	0·13	0·40
Moss	3·8	0	0·04	0·13	0·04	0·05	0·09	0·01	0·16	0·50

— denotes less than 0·01 milli equivalents per litre

61

and will accumulate weakly conjugated to whatever anions are being supplied to the system. The hydrological and ionic conditions slowly change, a change which is paralleled by a change in the biotic component of the system.

Acceptance of the basic idea of a theory of mire succession does not mean that all mires pass through the complete successional sequence. Wherever specific hydrological and/or ionic conditions exist within the confines of the definitions of mire template set out above, a mire ecosystem will develop the biota which will be characteristic of the ground water conditions prevailing at that time. The exact flora and fauna will depend on the phytogeographic/zoogeographic position of the region in which the mire is situated.

Plate 3.1.   Beaver pool near Parry Sound, Ontario, Canada. The beaver dam has caused lateral paludification overflooding an old muskeg and killing off the mire forest. New mire development is beginning on the surface of the pool

NORMAL HYDROSERAL DEVELOPMENT

The mire template can be changed in another way. At any stage in the mire hydrosere, deposition can raise the peat surface up above the permanent level of the mire water table. If this happens peat formation will cease, the mire will be invaded by shrubs and trees, eventually passing over to mire forest. (Further paludification can take place flooding the forest and thus producing layers of wood peat which, if the process is gradual, can be of considerable thickness (Radforth[33]). Such paludification can be brought about by climatic change (cf. the recurrence surfaces, see Chapter 6), by geomorphological changes, by the natural processes of mire development or by the action of beavers (see Plate 3.1) or by man.

It should therefore be possible to relate any mire studied, not only to its position in the mire hydrosere, but also to its position in the normal hydroseral succession which passes from open water to closed forest. The following stages of the normal hydrosere are recognised by physiognomy which is dependent on the life form of the dominant plants.

1. Floating aquatics, megaplankton.
2. Rooted aquatics with floating leaves.
3. Large perennials protruding from shallow water.
4. Smaller perennials (mainly sedges) forming dense closed mats.
5. Shrubs.
6. Trees.

Again it is emphasised that acceptance of the basic concept of a process of succession does not mean that every mire must necessarily pass through the sequence. Development can in fact start and terminate at any stage, and during the process stages can be omitted or repeated depending on factors which effect the hydrology of the site other than the accrual of peat.

As a generalisation, it would seem reasonable to state that any mire can pass through the following four stages.

Stage 1: open, where the surface of the peat is below the surface level of the ground water.

Stage 2: closed, where the vegetation forms a closed mat of roots and rhizomes at the surface of the ground water table,

Stage 3: building, where the peat is building up above the ground water level.

Stage 4: 'climax', where no further deposition of peat is taking place.

The biotic makeup of any mire system must therefore depend upon a combination of the hydrological and ionic conditions prevailing at the site and the level of the peat surface in relation to the fluctuations of the ground water table.

CLASSIFICATION OF MIRES ON BIOTIC CHARACTERS

To date the most comprehensive attempt to contain the biotic variety of mire systems into a single classification based on their constituent biota is *The genetical classification of the mires of the central European lowlands,* Tolpa *et al*[34]. Their classification is based on 141 characters which are the plant species found as subfossil material forming the peat.

The classification recognises 61 types of peat and hence 61 peat forming plant communities at the level of the association or below. For a brief account of phytosociology see part two of the appendix appearing at the end of this chapter on page 81. Twenty-eight of these mire communities are classified as Niedermoore (rheophilous), ten as Ubergangsmoore (transition) and nineteen as Hochmoore (ombrophilous). The classification is shown in Table 3.10. Although it is purely floristic, the stages in the two successional sequences are identifiable and are indicated on the tables.

Of the 61 peat types, 57 are widespread, being found throughout Europe, the remaining 4 (which are grouped into the Order Ericetalia tetralicis) are only found along the Atlantic seaboard of Europe where the species which characterise the order, namely *Erica tetralix, Trichophorum caespitosum, Juncus squarrosus, Narthecium ossifragum, Sphagnum compactum* and *Gymnocolea inflata* are found. The Atlantic oceanic component of the flora of western Europe is well documented (Praeger[27]) and it might be expected that it would be well represented in the vegetation of the ombrophilous mires, the mineral supply to which is the rain falling directly on them.

It was Du Rietz[28] and Witting[21, 22, 25] who first investigated the change in the flora of ombrogenous mires passing westwards across Scandinavia. Apart from the phytogeographical changes mentioned above, certain species such as *Sphagnum papillosum, S. imbricatum, S. magellanicum* and *S. rubellum* which are found only in poor fens (transition mires) in the east of Sweden become important members of the vegetation of the mosses (ombrophilous mires) of the south west of the country.

The extreme effect is found in western Ireland where *Schoenus nigricans* and *Molinia caerulea* are characteristic components of the ombrophilous mire flora, whereas in the central continent they are restricted to rheophilous mires. In the same way *Scorpidium scorpioides,* which is regarded in Scandinavia as an indicator of rich fen, is often abundant in transition mire in both the west of Scotland and the west of Ireland. Figure 3.3 summarises the main ecogeographical trends in ombrophilous mires passing north west across Europe. A number of hypotheses have been put forward to account for the ecogeographical

TABLE 3.10 a

Stage in Hydrosere	A	A.B		B		B – C	
Peat Type	Potamioni	Limno-phragmitioni		Magnocaricioni		Bryalo-parvocaricioni	
Peat Sub Type	Tyrfopel	Scirpo-typhaeti · Glycerieti · Equiseteti · Phragmiti		Cariceto-phragmiteti · Cariceti	Cladieti	Bryaleti · Cariceto-bryaleti	Gramini-cariceti
Hydrological Mire Type	1 3 2	1 2 3 3 1	3 4 3	3 1 1 1 1 1	4 3 2 1	3 3 3 2 1	3 3

Potamogeton lucens							
Potamogeton perfoliatus							
Nuphar luteum							
Nymphaea alba							
Myriophyllum verticillatum							
Ceratophyllum demersum							
Stratiotes aloides							
Hydrocharis morsus ranae							
Potamogeton natans							
Lemna minor							
Lemna trisulca							
Schoenoplectus lacustris							
Typha angusti et latifolia							
Glyceria aquatica							
Equisetum limosum							
Phragmites communis							
Carex rostrata							
Carex Hudsonii							
Carex pseudocyperus							
Carex paniculata							
Carex gracilis							
Carex acutiformis							
Cladium mariscus							
Lycopus europaeus							
Lysimachia thyrsiflora							
Cicuta virosa							
Ranunculus lingua							
Drepanocladus vernicosus							
Camptothecium nitens							
Paludella squarrosa							
Calliergon giganteum							
Scorpidium scorpioides							
Carex diandra							
Carex lasiocarpa							
Carex canescens							
Carex fusca							
Drepanocladus aduncus							
Drepanocladus intermedius							
Carex flava							
Calamagrostis neglecta							
Carex panicea							
Menyanthes trifoliata							
Comarum palustre							
Agrostis canina							
Eriophorum angustifolium							
Bryum ventricosum							
Acrocladium cuspidatum							
Caltha palustris							
Epilobium palustre							
Ranunculus flammula							
Aulacomnium palustre							
Helodium lanatum							
Sphagnum teres							
Meesea triquetra							
Campylium stellatum							
Festuca rubra							

Constancy: 1 · 2 · 3 · 4 · 5

Proportion (cover): 6 · 7 · 8 · 9

TABLE 3.10 b

Stage in Hydrosere	A								B								C					B		
Main Peat Type	Minero-sphagnioni								Ombro-sphagnioni													Ericioni		
Sub Types	Sphagno-cariceti						Sphagno-scheuchzerieti		Cuspidato-sphagneti			Eusphagneti		Eriophora-sphagneti		Pino-sphagneti						Ericaceti	Trico-phore-ti	
Hydrological Mire Type	6	5	5	5	6	6	5	6	7	7	6	7	7	7	7	7	7	7	7	7	7	6	7	7

Menyanthes trifoliata
Comarum palustre
Calliergon stramineum
Eriophorum angustifolium
Carex lasiocarpa
Carex rostrata
Carex canescens
Rhynchospora alba
Carex limosa
Scheuchzeria palustris
Drepanocladus fluitans
Sphagnum cuspidatum
Sphagnum balticum
Sphagnum recurvum
Oxycoccus quadripetalus
Drosera rotundifolia
Andromeda polifolia
Aulacomnium Palustre
Polytrichum strictum
Sphagnum rubellum
Sphagnum magellanicum
Sphagnum fuscum
Sphagnum papillosum
Eriophorum vaginatum
Pinus silvestris
Ledum palustre
Vaccinium uliginosum
Calluna vulgaris
Empetrum nigrum
Pleurozium Schreberi
Sphagnum nemoreum
Erica tetralix
Trichophorum caespitosum
Sphagnum compactum
Juncus squarrosus

Constancy

1   2   3   4   5

Proportion (cover)

6   7   8   9

The 'fitting' of the peat 'associations' to the hydrological mire types 1—7 and the stages of hydroseral development are based on the author's (D.J.B.) knowledge of the ecology of European mires gained from working with Jasnowski.

TABLE 3.10 c

Stage in Hydrosere	C	C		D	D	D
Main Peat Type	Alnioni			*Betulioni*	*Ledo pinioni*	
Sub Types	Salicetti		*Alneti* / *Alnobetuleti*	*Betuleti*	Pineti	
Hydrological Mire Type	3	4	4	1	3	5	7	7

Salix cinerea et aurita
Betula humilis
Myrica gale
Alnus glutinosa
Dryopteris thelypteris
Calamagrostis canescens
Lysimachia vulgaris
Acrocladium cuspidatum
Solanum dulcamara
Lycopus europaeus
Iris pseudoacorus
Peucedanum palustre
Phragmites communis
Carex acutiformis
Carex elongata
Carex riparia
Salix rosmarinifolia
Frangula alnus
Sphagnum squarrosum
Sphagnum palustre
Rubus idaeus
Sorbus aucuparia
Sphagnum fimbriatum
Betula pubescens
Deschampsia flexuosa
Polytrichum commune et formusum
Trientalis europaea
Pinus silvestris
Vaccinium myrtillus
Vaccinium uliginosum
Vaccinium vitis idaea
Pleurozium Schreberi
Dicranum undulatum
Molinia coerulea
Ledum palustre
Eriophorum vaginatum
Empetrum nigrum
Oxycoccus quadripetalus
Sphagnum nemoreum
Hylocomnium splendens
Calluna vulgaris
Sphagnum magellanicum
Sphagnum recurvum
Andromeda polifolia
Rubus chamaemorus

Constancy 1 2 3 4 5
Proportion (cover) 6 7 8 9

67

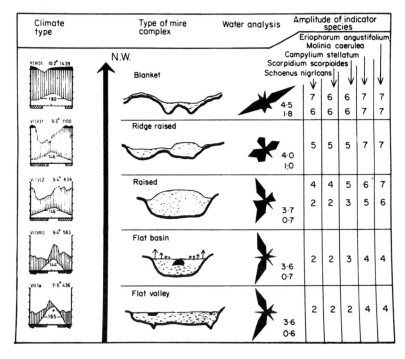

Figure 3.3. Ecogeographical differences between some European ombrophilous mires. Maucha diagrams for the mean analysis of waters of each type are shown, for explanation see caption to Figure 3.2. The upper figure beside each diagram is pH, the lower the total ionic concentration in milli equivalents per litre. The amplitude of certain mire species across the seven hydrological mire types in each region is shown

differences, especially for the seemingly anomalous flora of the blanket mires of western Ireland. The most widely accepted being that the more westerly mires receive greater amounts of minerals in the form of sea salt entrained in the onshore winds (Pearsall and Lind[35], Witting[21], Gorham[36]).

Study of the lowland mires of Ireland throws some light on the problem (Bellamy and Bellamy[37]). Figure 3.4 shows the distribution of ombrophilous mires studied in Ireland. The ombrophilous mires fall into two distinct groups, those of the cupolas of the ridge raised mire systems of the central Irish plain which are dominated by *Eriophorum vaginatum* and lack *Schoenus nigricans* and those of the western blanket mires in which the reverse is true. Consideration of the group of ombrophilous mires which are floristically intermediate between the two groups helps to clarify the position.

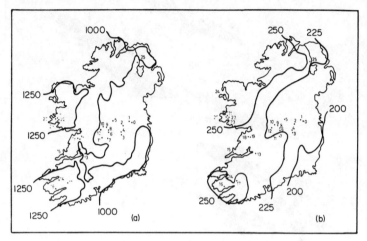

Figure 3.4. Distribution of ombrophilous mires studied in Ireland. (a) shows 'isohyets' for rainfall (mm) and (b) for the number of rain days

Kilkee (15) lies close to the sea in a very exposed position, a fact that is reflected in the ionic composition of its waters: total ionic concentration 2.2 m equiv/litre (higher than any of the blanket mires), with an overwhelming predominance of sodium and chloride. However, the flora of the mire resembles closely that of the ridge raised mires of the central plain, except for the presence of *Cladium mariscus* and *Molinia caerulea*.

Killorglin (14) lies further from the sea in a more sheltered position; total ionic concentration 2·01 m equiv/litre, yet its flora closely resembles that of the blanket mires, except for the presence of *Eriophorum vaginatum* and *Sphagnum pulchrum* and the paucity of *Sphagnum subsecundum.*

Clonbaell (7); *Castle Connell* (13); *Fallahogy* (25). These mires are situated at various distances from the sea, and differ floristically from the ombrophilous mires proper in the presence of *Carex rostrata* (7, 25), *Juncus effusus* (25), *Sphagnum pulchrum* (13), and *S. squarrosum* (25) on their mire plains.

The simple explanation of sea spray is therefore ruled out, lending weight to Gorham's observation in the English lake district (Gorham[39]) 'that sodium, potassium and chloride concentrations far greater than

69

normal are found in acid bogs very near the sea shore, without obvious floristic effects'.

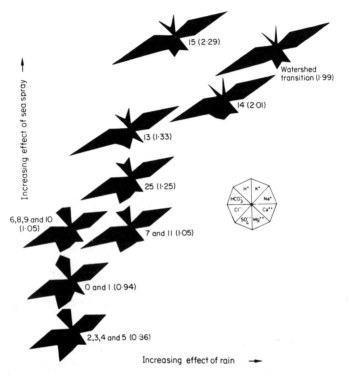

Figure 3.5. Ionic diagrams of the mean analysis of the water collected from the range of ombrotrophic mires studied in Ireland. The numbers beside each diagram refer to the mires as numbered on the maps in Figure 3.4. Western blanket mires are Nos 20-24. The numbers in brackets are the mean total ionic concentration in milli equivalents per litre. The increasing effect of sea spray is assessed subjectively from the position of the mires. For an explanation of the diagrams see the caption of Figure 3.2.

Figure 3.5 shows the differences between the ionic composition of the surface waters of the various types and groups of ombrophilous mire recognised above. The effect of increasing influence of sea spray, (assessed subjectively on consideration of the location of the mires) is plotted vertically; the increasing influence of rainfall (amount and duration) is plotted horizontally. Arrangement of the mires on grounds of floristic similarity follows the arrangement of the mires along the axis of increasing effects of rain, the following series being recognisable.

< 1000 mm rain; < 225 rain days per year
Ombrophilous mires proper, Ir. 1 to 6, 8, 9, 10 and 12.

< 1000 mm rain; < 250 > 225 rain days per year
Ombrophilous intermediate type, Ir. 7, 11, 13 and 25.

< 1250, > 1000 mm rain; < 250 > 225 rain days per year
Kilkee Ir. 15.

> 1250 mm rain; < 250 > 225 rain days per year
Killorglin. Ir. 14.

> 1250 mm rain; > 250 rain days per year
Blanket mires, Ir. 20 to 24.

The general trend is that with increasing 'effect of rainfall' there is a decrease in the importance of sulphate and hydrogen ions in the chemical makeup of the mire water and under the most extreme conditions an increase in the proportion of dissolved bicarbonate, the pH of the mire water rising above 4·5. The similar albeit more pronounced trend in the water chemistry of mires with increasing effect of ground water flow described above must be noted. Whether this factor alone can account for the ecogeographical differences between the Atlantic and Continental mires is impossible to say. However, it would seem reasonable to conclude that atmospheric flushing is a very real ecological factor, especially in areas with high and prolonged rainfall close to the western seaboard of Ireland.

This study lends weight to Kulczynski's[29] assumption 'that the mobility of the bog water is the most important factor controlling the edaphic conditions within the mire and hence the mire type' and poses the following question. Does the ecological importance of water flow lie in its supplying 'something' to the mire or in removing 'something' from the mire? Although of more than semantic importance the question does in part revolve around correct terminology, the following choices appear to be open.

| OMBROGENOUS | OMBROTROPHIC | OMBROPHILOUS |
| SOLIGENOUS | MINEROTROPHIC | RHEOPHILOUS |

It was Du Rietz[39] who replaced the suffix -genous which refers to the conditions of mire initiation with -trophic meaning mineral nourished. As the word mineral includes all plant nutrients, on purely semantic grounds it would appear better to adhere to the Kulczynski system or modify the Du Rietz terminology to *rheotrophic,* signifying nourished by the flow.

Sjörs[40,41] showed that intermediate fen vegetation and even 'moderately rich fen' vegetation could develop in very dilute solution provided that its acidity was moderate. He, however, makes it quite clear that rich fen vegetation is much more abundant in calcareous landscapes than in those dominated by acidic bed rock. The importance of flow and dissolved bases is thus made clear. The following examples indicate the close interrelationship which must exist between these two factors.

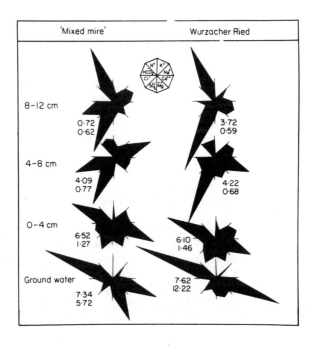

Figure 3.6. Ionic diagrams of ground water and water extracts prepared from 4 cm sections of a core removed from the centre of a miniature mire, and from water collected from the four corresponding vegetation types in the Wurzacher Ried S. Germany. For an explanation of the ionic diagrams see the caption of Figure 3.2. Upper figure beside each diagram is pH, lower figure the total ionic concentration in milli equivalents per litre

Mixed Mires

Mixed mire is a type of mire complex which is more commonly found in higher latitudes and altitudes, in which *Sphagnum fuscum* and *S. plumulosum* can invade flowing ground water producing large hummocks which can be regarded as miniature domed ombrotrophic mires. Figure 3.6 shows data from one of these hummocks which is situated in the main flow line from a spring which is discharging base rich water. The water is in fact so rich in dissolved bicarbonate that the spring head is marked by a large tufa mound. The whole area of rheotrophic mire is dotted with developing hummocks, species of moss such as *Campylium stellatum* and *Cratoneuron falcatum* deflect the main flow of ground water by growing up into large swelling tufts. It is in the middle of these tufts that the Sphagna first gain their foothold. The hummock enlarges, affecting a greater area and shutting off all effects of flowing ground water. Chemical analysis of water extracts from peat taken at different heights in the hummock (see Figure 3.6) shows that only 8 cm above the present ground water level ombrotrophic conditions prevail in the hummock indicating that there is no transfer of mineral rich water through the hummock. Table 3.11 gives full analytical data for the total mineral content of the hummock. Summing the totals of each mineral present above the 8 cm level gives a figure for total ombrotrophic mineral storage. If this represents solely supply from the rain, it is equivalent to that of some 40 years. It is interesting to note that from production studies the age of the hummock was estimated to be approximately 42 years (Bellamy and Reiley[42]). Until a complete mineral budget has been drawn up for the system, conclusions are sheer speculation. The work does, however, show that peat has the capacity to lock up many of the nutrients available to it.

Aapamires

The second example is the exact reverse, dealing with what are some of the largest mire complexes to be found in the world, the aapamires of Finland. Within the aapamire zone even the most extensive complexes are largely minerotrophic, *sensu* Du Rietz. The explanation is in all probability a combination of the following:

1. Aapamires are typically formed in gently sloping terrain, their growth depending upon a catchment which is large enough to provide an adequate supply of water throughout the growing period, the water gradually draining down-slope through the flarks and pools which are dominated by associations rich in minerotrophic-rheotrophic indicator species. In the aapamire zone, the terrain will be frozen for a considerable part of the

73

TABLE 3.11
TOTAL ANALYSIS DATA MINIATURE MIRE (AFTER BELLAMY AND RIELEY[42])

Height of sample above the base of the hummock cm	Floristic data — All identifiable material listed in order of importance in the sample (Sphagnum fuscum) dominant in all except the 0–4 cm level	Per Gram Dry Weight							
		Dry Weight g	Calorific Values kcal	Total Calcium mg	Total Magnesium mg	Total Potassium mg	Total Sodium mg	Total Phosphorus mg	pH m. equiv./ litre
52–55	Calluna vulgaris								3·96
	Pleurozium schreberi ………	4·74	4·826	11·23	1·23	3·08	0·71	0·24	0·110
48–52	Calluna vulgaris								3·68
	Oxycocus palustris ………	3·98	4·862	2·73	1·19	2·43	0·53	0·23	0·209
44–48	Oxycocus palustris ………	3·94	4·884	1·70	0·92	0·49	0·39	0·16	3·71 / 0·195
40–44	Calluna vulgaris ………………	3·99	4·716	1·35	0·72	0·41	0·38	0·10	3·71 / 0·195
36–40	Calluna vulgaris ………………	4·01	4·710	1·03	0·65	0·52	0·54	0·12	3·63 / 0·234
32–36	Calluna vulgaris ………………	4·03	4·601	1·13	0·71	0·57	0·54	0·13	3·46 / 0·347

Depth	Species									
28–32	Phragmites communis / Carex sp.	3.64	4.526	1.42	0.74	0.57	0.48	0.12	3.40	0.398
24–28	Phragmites communis	3.42	4.566	1.50	0.96	0.49	0.60	0.13	3.62	0.240
16–20	Carex sp. / C. panicea (fruit)	3.84	4.807	1.67	1.00	0.56	0.34	0.15	3.70	0.200
16–20	Carex sp.	4.31	4.536	1.36	0.90	0.68	0.46	0.16	3.40	0.398
12–16	Carex sp.	3.18	4.610	1.70	0.90	0.65	0.36	0.19	3.61	0.245
8–12	Carex sp. / C. panicea (fruit)	3.40	4.646	1.89	0.83	1.06	0.33	0.24	3.72	0.191
4–8	Sphagnum palustre / Carex sp. C. rostrata (fruit)	3.69	4.703	5.72	2.02	0.52	0.60	0.17	3.98	0.105
0–4	Sphagnum palustre, Campylium stellatum, Cratoneuron falcatum, Carex sp.	5.33	4.555	27.70	4.88	0.41	1.88	0.22	6.52	0.000
	Total for the complete core (area 50 cm^2)	55.50	259.90	288.04	75.37	50.84	34.47	9.45		

year and the growing period and period of melt water drainage will coincide.

2. Frost action, both within the mire and on the catchment will continuously expose new parent material to leaching, thus helping to maintain the supply of minerals to the mire water.

3. The shorter growing period will be correlated with a slow rate of peat growth and accumulation which, as shown on page 40 , can be zero in the flarks and pools. In such mire systems only very small amounts of minerals will be locked up in the peat deposit, this in itself must help in the continued supply of the biota.

It is interesting to note that in the ridge raised complexes of central Ireland (the peat deposits of which average between 10 and 13 m deep) minerotrophic mire is restricted to the margins of streams. The monotony of the vegetation of the great cupolas is relieved only where influent drains and watertracks bring water from the surrounding higher mineral terrain onto the mire expanse. In these mire complexes ombrotrophic peat formation is the dominant process, locking up all free minerals. In contrast in the western Irish blanket mires (where the average depth of the peat is between 1.5 and 6 m) minerotrophy is widespread. Here the milder Atlantic climate, coupled with heavy rainfall which can act as an active agent of peat erosion (Bowen[43]) results in a slower rate of peat accumulation. This, together with the atmospheric flushing described above (page 70), must help to maintain a high surface flux of minerals, and here the smallest effluent watertrack, or internal drainage system, is easily picked out by an abrupt change in vegetation.

In conclusion, it would appear that any factor which can stop the accumulation of the byproducts of the metabolism of the mire plants will arrest the main processes of change of the mire template. For further discussion of this point see this chapter, page 58.

There is little doubt that the mobility of the mire water must be the most important factor and therefore it is suggested that the terms *ombrotrophic, mesotrophic* and *rheotrophic* should be used to distinguish the three main groups.

It is also obvious that the floristic group which is characteristic of one particular phase in one of the successional series could well be masked by the other or by phytogeographical or ecogeographical variation. This could well account for some of the difficulty experienced in assigning certain of the phytosociologist's peat taxa to a single hydrological mire type, see Table 3.10.

Figure 3.7 shows data from a complete matrix of mire types studied in the Mazurian Lake District of Poland. Each mire was assigned to its hydrological mire type subjectively by reference to large scale maps and by detailed study in the field; phytosociological data were then collected and samples of ground water were taken for analysis. The similarity of the concentration and ionic makeup of the waters in each hydrological mire type throughout the four phases of hydroseral development is of great ecological interest.

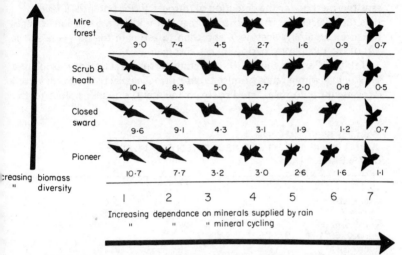

Figure 3.7.   Ionic diagrams of water collected from a full range of hydrological mire types in each stage of normal hydroseral development from the Mazurian Lake District of Poland. The figure below each diagram is the total ionic concentration in milli equivalents per litre

The fact that only three main climax vegetation types are recognisable is again of great interest, pointing to the fact that as the standing crop and hence the structural features of the vegetation increase (e.g. as biotic features take over an important role in the makeup of the habitat templates) the abiotic features become less important in determining the makeup of the biotic component of the ecosystem.

NITROGEN FIXATION IN MIRE ECOSYSTEMS

One geochemical requires special consideration as its continued availability to the ecosystem is dependent upon the presence and activity of a single enzyme complex within the ecosystem. The enzyme complex is nitrogenase and the biogeochemical is nitrogen, which is a key component of amino acids and proteins.

Indirect evidence for the possibility of nitrogen fixation in mires is found from the numerous reports of the presence of azotobacter in these systems, e.g. Stout[44].

The enzyme complex nitrogenase has low specificity and catalyses the reduction of a variety of substrates including acetylene. Discovery of the latter had a stimulating effect on research into nitrogen fixation, because acetylene reduction provided an inexpensive, simple and very sensitive method for the detection of nitrogen fixing potential (Stewart[45]). It is only necessary to expose the material under investigation to a gas mixture containing acetylene and then to estimate the ethylene at the end of the incubation period by gas chromatography.

Table 3.12 shows the results of a study of the detection of nitrogenase activity in a whole range of mire types. Nitrogenase activity was detected in every mire complex studied from the embryo systems close to the

TABLE 3.12
SUMMARY OF ACETYLENE REDUCTION ON ALL MIRE COMPLEXES STUDIED

Location	Date	$T(°C)$	O	T	R	N
Axel Heiberg Canada,78°12′W, 90°00′W	10.8	20	—	0.7 (0.2)	—	3
Nordkjosbotn Norway, 69°14′N, 19°34′E	10.8	20	—		1.7	10
Achmelvich Scotland, 58°16′N, 5°23′W	9.4	5	0	0.3 (0.1)	1.5 (0.3)	50
Din Moss Scotland, 56°41′N, 3°21′W	22.4	10	0	0.5 (0.2)	1.3 (0.2)	40
Sunbiggin Tarn England, 54°30′N, 2°20′W	30.12	16	0	7.9 (6.8)	26.4 (10.1)	62
Roydon Common England, 52°45′N, 0°24′E	21.8	20	—	31.2 (15.0)	55.7 (10.5)	62
Redgrave Fen England, 52°30′N, 0°45′E	21.8	20	—	—	31.4 (5.1)	40
Wurzacher Ried Germany, 47°44′N, 9°54′E	5.7	17	—	—	1.2 (0.1)	115
Vorsee Germany, 47°50′N, 9°40′E	30.6	17	—	0.2 (0.1)	—	35
Pfruhl Moss Germany, 47°35′N, 10°45′E	18.7	18	0	0.2 (0.1)	3.2 (0.9)	245
Pfruhl Moss Germany, 47°35′, 10°45′E	28.9	16	0	—	43.6 (15.2)	55

All results expressed in nMC_2H_4/day/mlitre fresh developing peat.
Date given is at time of sampling.
$T(°C)$ is approximate average temperature over period of incubation.
O = ombrotrophic, T = transition, R = rheotrophic, N = number of assays performed on complex. Figure in brackets standard error of the mean, $p = 0.05$.

permanent icecap on Axel Hieberg Island in the Canadian Arctic 78°12′N to Pfruhl Moss 47°35′N. Intersite comparison is impossible owing to the different climatic conditions prevalent at the sites during study. Intrasite comparison is valid and shows that in every case where data were collected there was no activity in ombrotrophic mires and maximum activity in the rheotrophic mires.

It is interesting to note that in central Europe (mire complex zones 2, 3, 4, 5 and 6) vascular plants with nitrogen fixing nodules, members of the Papilionaceae and the genus *Alnus,* are confined to rheotrophic mires. However, passing north westwards (see this chapter page 66), *Myrica gale* which has nitrogen fixing nodules (Bond[46]) makes its appearance first in rheotrophic and transition mires becoming more abundant until finally in the west of Scotland and especially western Ireland (mire complex zones 7B and 8B) it is found in abundance as a member of the flora of ombrotrophic mires. No nitrogenase activity was detected in the western Irish ombrotrophic peats dominated by *Schoenous nigricans.*

It must be emphasised that reduction of acetylene does not *per se* indicate the presence of active nitrogen fixation. The above investigations have however been backed up by studies using N^{15} and by use of substances which are known to stimulate and to inhibit bacterial fixation (Waughman and Bellamy[47]). Bacteria have also been isolated from the peat, and in pure nitrogen free cultures have been shown to grow and to reduce acetylene. The relation between the nitrogenase activity and mire hydrology is being actively investigated. It does appear safe to conclude, even at this stage of the investigation, that the supply of nitrogen may well be a factor which is limiting the biological potential of ombrotrophic mires.

SUMMARY AND SYNTHESIS

The abiotic template is translated at two levels into the phenomena of the living mire which are further modified by biotic — abiotic interactions.

Level 1

Geomorphology, hydrology and macroclimate effecting the gross morphology of the mire complex.

Level 2

Hydroedaphic conditions affecting the biotic expression of the component peat forming ecosystems.

79

BIOTIC-ABIOTIC INTERACTION

Biotic modification changes the abiotic template in two directions:

1. Modifying the hydroedaphic conditions and bringing about the changes of mire succession rheotrophic — ombrotrophic.
2. Modifying the climate near the ground, especially the ground water hydrology and hence bringing about changes from pioneer aquatic to mesic climax systems.

The exact biotic expression will be determined by the phytogeographical and zoogeographical location of the mire and hence the state of organic evolution on the global scale.

One point of clarification is needed regarding the relationships between the primary, secondary and tertiary nomenclature introduced in Chapter 2 and the terms rheotrophic, transition and ombrotrophic used in Chapter 3. It is obvious that the two systems are linked, but they are not strictly synonymous. For instance, although ombrotrophic mires must by definition be tertiary systems, both rheotrophic and transition mires can be either primary or secondary.

Owing to the difficulty of using these long terms in the construction of sentences, it is suggested that the shorter terms 'bog', 'poor fen' and 'fen' are retained, being defined as follows: Bog ≡ Ombrotrophic, Poor fen ≡ Transition, and Fen ≡ Rheotrophic; Peats and mire systems are defined in this chapter.

APPENDIX

Spring Mires

Mires formed in situations over spring heads are called *spring mires*. All spring mires are rheotrophic as they receive water from underground aquifers, that is from outside their immediate catchment. Two types are recognised, those developed in base poor and those developed in base rich waters. Both may exhibit a convex profile, the height of the convex peat mass being a function of the hydrostatic head of the spring and the containing volume of the peat.

The term spring mire is best reserved for convex peat systems formed directly over spring heads. In cases where the peat deposit forms downslope of such a spring or in relation to a diffuse seepage area the term *hanging mire (hangmire)* is best used.

The largest spring mires are those formed over base rich springs when the growth mechanism is more complex. Water supersaturated with bicarbonate reacts with the acidic byproducts of the mire plants precipitating a tufa like substance. The profile of these mires consists of bands of tufa interspersed by bands of lime rich peat. Such tufa mires may reach heights in excess of 10 m (Bitner[46]).

Spring mires may be found throughout the mire zones of the world but like hangmires they are more abundant in the arctic and subarctic areas. For more general accounts see Havas[47] and Kukla[48].

Phytosociology

Phytosociology is a method for the description and classification of vegetation based on the floristic content of unit descriptions (Aüfnahmen) (Braun Blanquet[49]). The basic taxon of the phytosociologist is the association which is recognised and characterised by certain species or groups of species which have high fidelity; that is, their occurrence is restricted to that association.

The taxa are given latin polynomials and the associations (suffix -etum) are grouped successively into alliances (-ion) orders (-etalia) and classes (-etea).

These methods and the resultant nomenclature have come under severe criticism, nevertheless they are today the most widely used and accepted 'language' of vegetation.

REFERENCES

1. CLARKE, F.W. 'Data of geochemistry.' *U.S. Geol. Survey Bull.* 770 (1930).
2. RODHE, W. 'The ionic composition of lake waters.' *Int. Ver. Limnol. Verh.* **10**, 377-386 (1949).
3. CONWAY, E.J. 'Mean geochemical data in relation to oceanic evolution.' *Roy. Irish Acad. Proc.* **B 48**, 119-159 (1942).
4. GORHAM, E. 'Factors influencing supply of major Ions to inland waters, with special references to the atmosphere.' *Geol. Soc. Amer. Bull.* **72**, 795-840 (1961).
5. HUTCHINSON, G.E. *A treatise on limnology.* J. Wiley & Son, New York. 1015 (1957).
6. WOODCOCK, A.H. 'Atmospheric salt particles and raindrops.' *J. Meterology,* **9**, 200-212 (1952).
7. MACKERETH, F.J.H. and HERON, J. p. 20-21 in *Freshwater Biol. Assoc. British Empire Ann. Report* No. 22, 63 (1954).
8. JUNGE, C.E. 'Atmospheric chemistry.' *Adv. Geophysics,* **4**, 1-108 (1958).
9. WINDOM, H.L. *Bull. Geol. Soc. Amer.* **80**, 761 (1969).
10. JENNY, H. *Factors of Soil Formation,* McGraw Hill, New York, 281 (1941).
11. ODUM, H.T. 'Trophic structure and productivity of Silver Springs, Florida.' *Ecol. Monogr.,* **27**, 55-112 (1957).
12. GORHAM, E. 'The ionic composition of some lowland lake waters from Cheshire England.' *Limnol. and Oceanog.* **2**, 22-27 (1957).
13. MORTIMER, C.H. 'The exchange of dissolved substances between mud and water in lakes.' J. Ecology. **30**, 147-201 (1942).
14. WALTERS, A.A. 'Nitrate in soil, plants and animals.' *J. Soil Assoc.* **16** No. 3, 1-22 (1968).

15. WEBER, C.A. 'Aufbau und Vegetation der Moore Norddeutschlands.' *Englers. Bot. Jahrb.* 90 Liepzig (1908).
16. POTONIE, R. 'Aufbau und Vegetation der Norddeutschlands.' *Englers. Bot. Jahrb.* 90 Liepzig (1908).
17. MELIN, E. Studier Över de Noorländska Handbibl. 7. Uppsala (1917).
18. SJÖRS, H. *Myrvegetation 1 Bergslagen* Almquist and Wiksells, Upsala, 299 (1948).
19. WEBER, C.A. *Das Moor Hanoverische Geschicht Blätter* (1909).
20. KIVINEN, E. 'Über Electrolytegehalt und Reaktion der Moorwässer.' *Maatouskoelatioksen Maatutkimusosasto Agrogeol. Julkaisuja.* 38. Helsingfors (1935).
21. WITTING, M. 'Katjonbestämningar I Myrvatten.' *Bot. Notiser,* Lund 287-304 (1947).
22. WITTING, M. 'Kalcium halten I nagra Nordsvenska Myrvatten.' *Svensk Bot. Tidskr., Uppsala,* **43,** 2-3 (1949).
23. DU RIETZ, E. 'Huvudenheter och Huvudgranser I Svensk Myrvegetation.' *Svensk Bot. Tidskr., Uppsala,* **43,** 2-3 (1949).
24. THUNMARK, S. 'Über rezente Eisenocker und ihre Mikroorganismengeme in-Schaften. *Akad. Avh. Bull. Geol. Inst. Uppsala.* 29 (1942)
25. WITTING, M. 'Forsatta Katjonbestamningar I Myrvatten.' *Svensk. Bot. Tidskr. Uppsala,* **42,** 116-134 (1948).
26. SJÖRS, H. 'On the relation between vegetation and electrolytes in North Swedish mire waters.' *Oikos* 2, 241-258 (1950).
27. PRAEGER, R.L.J. *The Botanist in Ireland.* Dublin (1934).
28. DU RIETZ, E.G. Dalamyrarna vid Klagstorpsåsen. "Satyryck ur Från Falbygd till Vänerkust" Utginen av Skaraborgs Läns Naturskyddsförenging (1947).
29. KULCZYNSKI, S. 'Peat Bogs of Polesie.' *Mem. Acad. Sci. Cracovie* B. 1-356 (1949).
30. BELLAMY, D.J. 'An ecological approach to the classification of the lowland mires of Europe.' *Proc. 3rd Int. Peat Cong. Quebec.* 74-79 (1968).
31. BRONSTED, J.N. 'The principle of specific interaction of ions.' *J. Am. Chem. Soc.* **45.** 2898-2910 (1923).
32. BELL, R.P. *Acids and Bases, their quantitative behaviour.* Methuen, London (1952).
33. RADFORTH, N.W. in MacFARLANE, I.C. *Muskeg Engineering Handbook,* Univ. Toronto Press. 297 (1969).
34. TOLPA, S. JASNOWSKI, M., and PALCZYNSKI, A. 'System der Genetischen Klassifizierung der Torfe Mitteleuropas.' *Zesz. Probl. Post. Navk. Roln.* Warsaw No. 76 (1967).
35. PEARSALL, W.H. and LIND, E. 'A note on a Connemara Bog type.' *J. Ecol.* **29,** 62-68 (1941).
36. GORHAM, E. 'On the chemical composition of some waters from the Moor House Nature Reserve.' *J. Ecol.* **44,** 377-384 (1956).
37. BELLAMY, D.J. and BELLAMY, S.R. 'An ecological approach to the classification of the lowland mires of Ireland. *'Proc. Royal Irish Acad.* **65 B,** 6 (1967).
38. GORHAM, E. 'The ionic composition of some bog and fen waters in the English Lake District.' *J. Ecol.* **44,** 142-152 (1956).
39. DU RIETZ, E. 'Die Mineral Bodenwasserzeigergrenze als Grundlage einer Naturlichen Zweigleiderung der Nord-und Mitteleuropaischen Moore.' *Vegetatio,* 5-6, 571-585 (1954).

40. SJÖRS, H. 'The mire vegetation of Upper Långaw District in Jämtland.' *Stockholm and Uppsala Ark. Bot.* **33A, 6**, 1-69 (1946).
41. SJÖRS, H. 'Regional Studies in North Swedish Mire Vegetation.' *Lund. Bot. Notiser.* **173,** 222 (1950).
42. BELLAMY, D.J. and RIELEY, J. 'Ecological statistics of a miniature bog.' *Oikos,* **18,** 33-40 (1967).
43. BOWER, M.M. 'The cause of erosion in Blanket Peat Bogs in the Southern Pennines.' *Scot. Geog. Mag.* **78,** 33-43 (1962).
44. BOND, G. 'Isotope studies of nitrogen fixation in non-legume root nodules.' *Annals of Botany N.S. XXI* **84,** 513-521 (1957).
45. WAUGHMAN, J. and BELLAMY, D.J. 'Potential Nitrogen Fixation in Some European Peatlands.' *Proc. 4th Int. Peat Cong. Helsinki.* **1,** 309-318 (1972).
46. BITNER, K. 'Pseudo- Krodliskowe torfowisko w okolicy sidry. Zeszyty Problemowe Post Nauk Roln.' *Zeszyty* **17** (1958).
47. HAVAS, P. 'Vegetation und Okologie der Ostfinnischen Hangmoore.' *Ann. Bot. Soc. Bot. Fen. 'Vanamo'* 31, 2, p. 188 (1961).
48. KUKLA, St. 'The development of the Spring Bogs in the region of N.E. Poland.' (English Summary 1. Polska). *Zeszyty Probelmowe Post. Akad Nauk Roln. Warsawa.* **57,** 481-495 (1965).
49. BRAUN BLANQUET, J. *Pflanzensozologie* 865, Springer Verlag Wien (1964).

Chapter Four

Mires – Peat Producing Ecosystems

Having looked at the basic structure of ecosystems in terms of their energy and nutrient relationships, we are now in a position to examine the special case of mire ecosystems. The most obvious feature of such systems is their wetness, but this physical character results in important modifications of the familiar process of energy flow and nutrient cycling, modifications involving the production of the material we term *peat*.

We shall be examining the structure and formation of this material in detail later, but for the moment it is sufficient for us to regard peat as the incompletely decomposed remains of plant and animal life accumulating at their site of growth under extremely wet conditions. The term *mire* we shall use to cover all wetland ecosystems where such peat accumulates. It excludes situations in which organic detritus accumulates as a result of water transport from their site of growth (*allochthonous* deposits) such as lakes and salt marshes. Mire peats then are built up in the very place where the plants and animals which compose them lived and grew: such peats can be termed *autochthonous.*

ENERGY IN MIRE ECOSYSTEMS

In the first chapter it was explained that energy first enters ecosystems by the process of photosynthesis, leading ultimately to the build up of plant material. This material may be eaten by herbivores or may die and pass into what is termed the 'decomposer' food chain. In most ecosystems the fate of material entering this food chain is to be broken down and respired by micro-organisms until it is completely dissipated. However, mire ecosystems have a decomposer food chain which is impaired as a result of extreme physical conditions, viz. wetness. As a result the process of decomposition is incomplete and some of the material which resulted from primary production accumulates in an undecomposed state. The total quantity of herbivores living in a mire at any given time is only a small fraction of the plant material present. It is not surprising, therefore, that there is a correspondingly smaller contribution of animal remains to the peat; however, a proportion of this secondary production (i.e. animal matter) also enters the decomposer chain and a proportion of this remains as peat.

The generalised scheme of energy flow through an ecosystem which was described in Chapter 1 must therefore be modified for the mire ecosystem (Figure 4.1). Thus when we consider the energy balance sheet

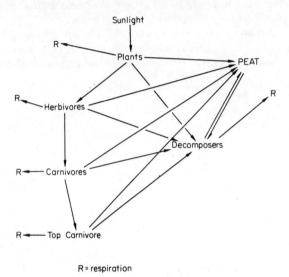

R = respiration

Figure 4.1.   Energy flow in a mire ecosystem

for such a system we find that not all of the energy entering the system is liberated by the respiration of the component organisms, nor is the remainder entirely to be accounted for in the process of succession and the accumulation of living material in the system. A component of the energy remains stored up in the peat, locked away until the restraining factor of excessive wetness is removed resulting in the energy becoming available to decomposers once more. This storage of a reserve of energy by mire ecosystems is of considerable importance since such 'fossil' energy can be tapped by man and released in combustion.

NUTRIENT CYCLES IN MIRE ECOSYSTEMS

A modification of energy flow within an ecosystem is invariably associated with changes in the pattern of nutrient cycling within the system. The dead organic material which goes to make up peat contains a proportion of the nutrient capital of the system and this also may remain in 'fossil' form while the peat remains undecomposed. Such nutrients are effectively removed from circulation and the process of peat formation must therefore be regarded as a drain upon the nutrient economy of the system. The retardation of the decomposition process as a result of adverse physical conditions slows down nutrient cycling in the system and this may result in severe nutrient deficiency in those systems which are poor in nutrients to begin with.

Some nutrients, e.g. carbon, may be present in abundance and easily available from the environment. The locking up of such elements in peat deposits does not represent a serious depletion of resources.

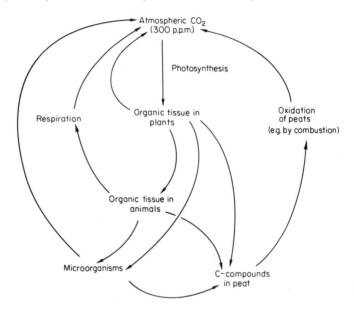

Figure 4.2.   Cycling of carbon in a mire ecosystem

Figure 4.2 shows the cycling of carbon in a mire ecosystem. The level of atmospheric CO_2 remains fairly constant though it varies both diurnally and seasonally[1]. It is buffered to a certain degree by dissolved bicarbonate in the oceans, though there is some evidence that recent burning of fossil fuels (largely oil and coal of considerably greater antiquity than peat deposits) may be raising the overall global level of CO_2.

Carbon fixation by green plants is, of course, directly related to the

86

process of primary productivity and further attention will be given to this shortly. It will vary with the vegetation involved and with climatic conditions, as will the relative importance of decomposer and consumer food chains.

Although the locking up of carbon in a peat deposit does not appreciably affect the quantity of that element available to the ecosystem, this is not true of all elements. Some others, e.g. nitrogen, may be in abundant supply but difficult to utilise whilst others, e.g. phosphorus, may be in short supply in the environment. These elements are also subject to the process of being rendered unavailable as they are incorporated into peat, but in this case the drain upon the nutrient economy of the entire system may be a significant one, depending upon:

1. how much of the element is locked up in a given quantity of peat
2. how fast the peat is being formed
3. the rate at which a new supply of the element enters the ecosystem.

In many terrestrial ecosystems, e.g. woodland, there are two main sources of input for a nutrient like phosphorus which is not present in gaseous form, first in solution or suspension in the precipitation and secondly released from rocks as they weather to form soil. Once a mire ecosystem has accumulated a thickness of peat too great for the roots of surface dwelling plants to penetrate, it is effectively insulated from the underlying geological substrate and the process of weathering *in situ* is no longer of importance as a source of nutrients. On the other hand the water input of a mire ecosystem may contain in solution ions which have resulted from rock weathering in adjacent ecosystems. Thus the hydrology of a mire is of paramount importance in the consideration of its nutrient regime.

Figure 4.3 gives a generalised scheme for the cycling of a nutrient element such as phosphorus. This scheme applies to those mires which receive drainage waters from surrounding areas, termed *rheotrophic* and *transition mires.* In certain other types of mire, termed *ombrotrophic* mires, the living organisms in the system are independent of all drainage water, often as a result of the development of a thick insulating layer of peat, and thus rely entirely upon precipitation and dust fallout as a source of nutrients (see Chapter 3). Even amongst rheotrophic mires there is considerable variation in the nutrient content of the drainage water input and the rate at which such water passes through the mire, both of which might be expected to influence its nutrients status. In particular the geology of the surrounding area probably has the main

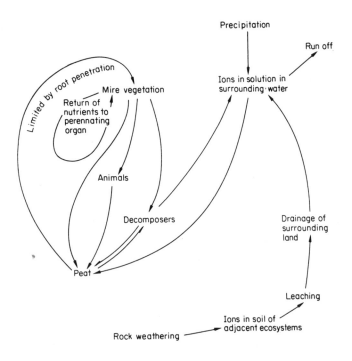

Figure 4.3. Cycling of phosphorus in rheophilus mire ecosystems and their surroundings.

influence upon the chemical composition of drainage water, together with the pattern of human land use.

One further aspect of the nutrient relations of peat forming ecosystems needs to be considered before we look in detail at some of the pathways discussed above. This relates to the physicochemical properties of the peat itself. Peat has a very high cation exchange capacity. This means that cations are retained in peaty material by various physicochemical forces which will be discussed later, and are not easily lost from the system by the process of leaching. This is in many ways analogous to the retention of cations by the clay minerals of terrestrial soils. This means that a high proportion of nutrients released into surface waters on the decomposition of organic tissue will not be lost in run off but will be retained in the surface layers. Similarly nutrients arriving in rain water may be stored in the system in this way. However, if such ions have not been incorporated into living plants before peat accretion renders them out of reach of the surface growing plants, then these will become unavailable, fossilised reserves. 'Fossil' peat then contains nutrient elements bound in undecomposed organic structures and also inorganic nutrient ions bound superficially.

Obviously peats vary in the degree to which their cation exchange capacity is saturated with cations other than hydrogen ('bases'). Rheotrophic peats which have developed under conditions with a rich supply of ions in their drainage may have a high percentage 'base' saturation, whereas in ombrotrophic peats, and in transition peats developed under *oligotrophic* conditions (i.e. where drainage water supply is poor in ionic content), the percentage 'base' saturation may be very low, all available sites being occupied by hydrogen ions.

This cation exchange capacity of peats has resulted in a demand for the commodity from the horticultural industry; a point which will be raised again when we consider commercial aspects of peatlands.

PRIMARY PRODUCTION IN PEATLANDS

Having outlined the two major ways in which peat producing ecosystems differ from the 'generalised ecosystem' described in Chapter 1, we must now look in greater detail at some of the processes taking place within them.

The first such process to be considered is that of primary production since this provides energy for the functioning of the ecosystem. Table 4.1 gives figures for the rates of production of dry matter in a variety of ecosystems in different climatic regions. The figures for the *Sphagnum* bog refer to bogs developed in forest clearings and it can be seen that the annual increase in dry matter for such situations is very low when compared with most other ecosystems. Of the vegetation types listed only arctic tundra and dwarf scrub deserts fall below the productivity level of a *Sphagnum* dominated bog. It is less than half as productive as coniferous forest and little more than a third as productive as deciduous oak woodland.

However, other peat producing ecosystems in temperate regions contrast very strongly with this type of mire. In particular the reed-swamp type of community is extremely productive, a *Scirpus lacustris* dominated swamp in Germany having an annual net production of 4600 g/m^2 (46 metric tons per hectare). A figure of this order indicates that reedswamp ecosystems are by far the most productive natural vegetation type of the temperate regions when expressed as gain in dry weight per unit ground area. It far exceeds most agricultural crop

TABLE 4.1
NET PRODUCTION IN VARIOUS ECOSYSTEMS, IN g/m²/ANNUM.
(AFTER RODIN AND BASILEVICH[7], WESTLAKE[8] AND FORREST[14]).

	Biomass (g/m²)	Net Production	Litter Fall
Afforested *Sphagnum* bog	3 700	340	250
Mangroves	12 730	930	—
Arctic tundra	500	c.100	c.100
Taiga fir forest	26 000	700	500
Temperate oak forest	40 000	900	650
Temperate steppe	2 500	1 120	1 120
Dwarf shrub desert	4 300	122	120
Savannah	6 660	c.1 200	c.1 150
Tropical rain forest	> 50 000	3 250	2 500
Reedswamp (temperate — *Scirpus lacustris*) Germany	—	4 600	—
Reedswamp (temperate — *Typha* hybrid) U.S.A.	—	2 900	—
Pennine blanket bog (*Eriphorum/Calluna*)	2 450	635	635

production rates, e.g. average wheat yield in a high production area (Netherlands) is 1250 g/m²/annum. It approximates to the production rates achieved by mass algal culture in Japan, i.e. 4530 gm/m²/annum.

Thus the overall production rates of peatlands can be seen to vary considerably between different systems within a given climate area. There are several reasons for this; in the first place, the growth form and robustness of the dominant plants involved in the two systems mentioned differ very considerably from one another, *Sphagnum*, being a moss, is small in stature, whilst *Scirpus* is a tall, robust plant capable of rapid, vigorous, rhizomatous growth. However, such a statement does not explain how two wetland habitats can so differ in their productivities. A fuller answer is to be found by considering the environmental potentialities for growth in the two situations and this term involves not only climatic factors but also nutrient supply. In the case of the *Sphagnum* bog we have ombrotrophic conditions with a very poor supply of nutrients which therefore limit the growth of the plants despite abundant water. Reedswamp, on the other hand, has an abundant nutrient supply in drainage water in addition to ample water. Thus productivity in mire ecosystems in general is probably limited by nutrient supply, though water supply may also be of importance to hummock dwelling species.

The measurement of productivity in peatlands, as in most other ecosystems, is complicated by the continuous passage of fixed energy along a variety of paths, the relative importance of each of which must be determined. Figure 4.4 shows in diagrammatic form the possible fates of energy fixed in the living parts of a mire plant.

Each box or compartment in this model represents an energy reservoir and the arrows represent paths of energy movement from one reservoir to another. In addition, energy is being lost from all of the living 'reservoirs' as a result of respiration (not indicated on the diagram).

The entire situation is further complicated by the fact that both the size of the reservoirs and the rates of energy flow between reservoirs will vary diurnally and seasonally with climate, as indeed will the rates of respiration. When it is considered that each species will have its own characteristic pattern of energy movement and storage it makes clear the immense amount of information required for the understanding of energy movement within even a simple ecosystem. It involves the measurement of the various reservoirs at frequent intervals together with an estimation of the rate of energy flow along each possible path, also at frequent intervals. It is not surprising that wherever such studies have been undertaken they have involved teams of specialised research

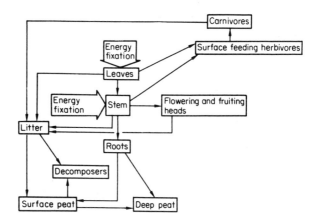

Figure 4.4. Flow of energy fixed in the living parts of a mire plant

workers involved with the collection of data and the use of analogue computers for the simulation of the system once the data have been collected.

Methods of Measurement

An abundance of literature now exists relating to the various methods available for the measurement of primary productivity together with their relative merits and demerits, hence no attempt will be made here to review this vast field. However, mention must be made of a few points relevant to the study of peat producing ecosystems.

Measurements of standing crop, i.e. the energy reservoirs within the vegetation have been made in a variety of mire habitats. These have usually been expressed in grams per unit area, but a more useful measure would be the energy content of these systems in terms of calories. Cropping studies have been carried out at various times of the year to obtain these figures, from which it is also often possible to estimate production rates of various plant organs. These studies, however, have been mainly confined to the above ground portions of plants which are most easily cropped.

Root biomass and root production figures for mire plants are much more difficult to obtain and are therefore scarcer in the literature. At one time it was standard practice to add a 40% correction factor for below ground parts, but this is not acceptable in modern critical studies. Such studies as have been undertaken on the root production of mire plants usually involve species with robust rhizomes such as the swamp dwellers, e.g. *Phragmites, Scirpus, Typha, Glyceria,* etc. These are more easily removed from the substratum than are fine rooted plants. Also their roots do not penetrate to the depths attained by some members of the Cyperaceae, e.g. *Eriophorum.* In these types the measurement of root productivity is exceedingly difficult[14].

Czechoslovakian workers[5] have followed and dated the growth of *Typha latifolia* rhizomes by observing the emergence of shoots and finally cropping and separating the below ground parts. Westlake[6] has considered the possibilities of sorting fragments of rhizomes into age classes according to morphology. All of these studies have found that the percentage biomass of reedswamp plants found underground varies very considerably even within a single species. Czechoslovakian workers have found values for *Typha* of about 60—70% biomass underground and for *Phragmites* some values in excess of 80%. Variable though these figures may be, it is evident that a very considerable proportion of these wetland plants exist beneath the ground surface where they must constitute a considerable drain upon the energy fixation resources of plants. An efficient translocation system is needed for the transport of the products of above ground photosynthesis to the regions of rhizome extension below ground.

An alternative method for measurement of productivity in plants is that of estimating gas exchange rates. This has been attempted on a variety of species and communities using both infrared gas analysis techniques and also labelled $^{14}CO_2$ as a tracer. Such studies have usually involved the enclosure of the plant or the system under study in a transparent plastic bag and this in itself raised the objection that microclimatic and gas flow conditions may be altered. In addition, such measurements are of necessity relatively short in duration, which makes it difficult to compute long term production rates.

An example may help to illustrate this problem. Walker and Waygood[9] studied the productivity of *Phragmites communis* in the field in a swamp in Manitoba. They measured the CO_2 consumption of a single shoot of this plant by means of supplying it with $^{14}CO_2$ at 300 p.p.m. in a transparent plastic bag and allowing it to photosynthesise for one hour. They were able to calculate that during this hour the entire shoot (leaves, sheaths and culm) had incorporated a total of 6.81 mg of carbon. They then estimated the density of *Phragmites* shoots in the marsh at 12.75 shoots/m². Assuming a ten hour day, the productivity of the reed population works out at 3.5 g carbon/m²/day. Thus the assumptions and sampling errors in such a calculation are considerable and seasonal variations in climate and therefore productivity make further extrapolation to annual production figures quite impossible without a great deal of extra data. However, such figures can be of great value when comparing the photosynthetic production of different wetland communities. For example Westlake gives values of 0.95 g carbon/m²/day for a *Ceratophyllum* population (submerged aquatic) and 6.0 g carbon/m²/day for *Typha*, which are of the same order as Walker and Waygood's figures for *Phragmites.*

Bryophytes, in particular mosses, can present additional problems in the study of the primary productivity of peatlands. This is of especial concern since one genus of mosses, viz. *Sphagnum* is probably the most important peat forming group of plants in the world. These plants have no roots, therefore all the problems of estimating root production are avoided, but their manner of growth is such that the upright stems elongate whilst the older portions below gradually die and enter the 'litter'. This latter process, being a gradual one, is difficult to measure, as is the entry of such dead material into the 'peat' proper. As Clymo[10] has pointed out in his review of methods of growth measurement in *Sphagnum*, the terms 'standing crop' and 'biomass' are meaningless when applied to this plant because of the difficulty in separating living plant from dead plant and dead plant from peat.

Clymo considers four main types of method of estimating growth in this plant, each of which has a number of variations when used by different workers.

1. The use of 'innate time markers' within the plant itself. For example, where there is a considerable seasonal variation in climate, there may be cyclic fluctuation in growth rate (not necessarily annual) greater growth occurring at favourable periods, e.g. autumn. Such cycles may be reflected in anatomical and morphological features which act as time markers. Over longer time periods ^{14}C in dead *Sphagnum* can also provide datings following the incorporation of the material into peat

2. The use of reference marks outside the plant, e.g. wires buried in profile to which *Sphagnum* extension can be related

3. The cutting of plants to a known length and subsequent length measurements — a process involving considerable disturbance to the plant

4. The direct measurement of changes in weight, which presents many technical difficulties. Clymo has overcome many of these by suggesting a technique for measuring weights of *Sphagna* whilst still immersed in water.

Obviously the results obtained from these different measurements will not be directly comparable with one another; some provide weight data for whole populations which can be expressed directly on a ground area basis, whereas others refer to weight or length increases in individual plants. The latter can be converted into expressions with a ground area basis if the density of shoots per unit surface area of ground is estimated.

TABLE 4.2
GROWTH RATES IN *SPHAGNUM* ESTIMATED BY METHOD 1 (SEE TEXT) AND EXPRESSED AS g/dm^2/annum.

Author	Species	Rate
Clymo (1970)[10]	S. papillosum	7
Clymo (1970)[10]	S. recurvum	9
Bellamy and Rieley (1967)[12]	S. fuscum	2.7
Turner (1964)[13] (after Clymo (1970)) using ^{14}C dating)	S. imbricatum	3

Table 4.2 gives some figures obtained from different species of *Sphagna* in different areas using method 1.

TABLE 4.3
GROWTH RATES IN *SPHAGNUM* ESTIMATED BY METHOD 4 (SEE TEXT) AND EXPRESSED AS g/dm^2/annum. RESULTS FROM THURSLEY COMMON, SURREY BY R.S. CLYMO[10].

Species	Position	Rate
S. rubellum	Hummock	4.3
S. rubellum	Lawn	3.2
S. cuspidatum	Pool	7.9
S. cuspidatum	Lawn	3.6
S. papillosum	Pool	6.1
S. papillosum	Hummock	3.1
S. recurvum	Pool	5.4
S. recurvum	Hummock	3.6

Table 4.3 gives some of Clymo's figures for four *Sphagnum* species at Thursley Common, Surrey, growing under varying microtopographic conditions. These measurements were all made using method 4.

The results in Table 4.3 demonstrate how variable growth rates within a given species of *Sphagnum* can be according to its precise situation. Bearing this variability in mind it can be seen that the results of Table 4.2 obtained by a different method are of the same order of magnitude. In comparison with these, Rodin and Basilevich[7] quote a figure of 3.4 g/dm^2/annum for *Sphagnum* in forest areas of Russia, while Overbeck and Happach[11] give a value of 16.6 g/dm^2/annum for a *Sphagnum recurvum* population. It is likely that the overall environmental factors which limit rates of production in *Sphagnum* communities are climate[10] and water table[11].

Different species of plant, then, require different techniques for the measurement of their productivities. However, under natural conditions it is unusual for any considerable area of ground to be occupied by a single species, therefore when we seek data upon the productivity of mire ecosystems, we need to have data concerning the growth rates of a variety of different plants in any given system. As an example, the blanket mires of the northern pennines are often dominated by such species as *Eriophorum vaginatum* and *Calluna vulgaris*, but mixed in

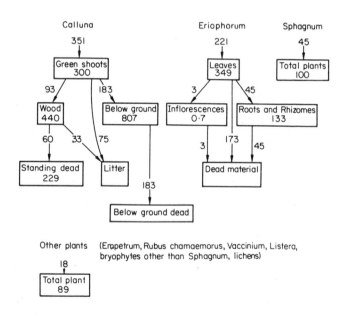

Figure 4.5. *Primary production in a Pennine blanket mire (Forrest[14]) Quantities are in g/m^2, rates in g/m^2/year. Microflora biomass[17] for Juncus squarrosus moor in same area = 28-197g wet weight/m^2 and fauna = 56-295g wet weight/m^2*

with these in varying proportions are such species as *Empetrum nigrum, Vaccinium myrtillus, Rubus chamaemorus,* etc. as well as *Sphagnum* spp. and various other bryophytes and lichens. An understanding of such an ecosystem requires not only a detailed knowledge of the two dominant species, but also data concerning the contribution of the less abundant species to the energy input of the entire system. A full energy flow sheet demands a knowledge of the growth and production rates of the component plants together with an estimate of their abundance in the ecosystem.

Figure 4.5 shows some results obtained from Moor House National Nature Reserve in Westmorland. This has been the site of intensive investigations into energy and nutrient relationships of blanket mires in connection with the International Biological Programme. G.I. Forrest's results (Figure 4.5) provide the basic data concerning the initial production of biological material and its distribution within the ecosystem. This illustrates the order of importance of various species in the pattern of production and it can be seen that the vast bulk of dry matter production is carried out by the two dominants. However, a great deal of variability was found, as might be expected, most especially in the abundance of the various species in different parts of the mire. These figures can therefore be regarded as mean values around which variations of up to 25% may occur.

THE MICROBIOLOGY OF PEATLANDS

As we have seen, a large proportion of the total matter produced in peatland ecosystems passes to the organisms termed 'decomposers'. The microbial population of the peat represents an important constituent group of decomposers in two main respects. In the first place their activity regenerates the nutrient elements built into organic tissue. The rate of release of these elements, which may well be a limiting factor for the growth of some ombrotrophic mire plants, is proportional to the rate of activity of the peat microflora. In the second place, the relationship between rate of litter production and rate of litter decomposition is the determining factor in the rate of peat formation.

In view of the importance of microbe populations in peatland ecology, it is therefore worth spending a little time considering some of their characteristic features.

In the first place, decomposition rates are frequently very low in peatlands when compared with other ecosystems[22]. This is especially true if

1. there is constant waterlogging
2. temperatures are generally low (i.e. high latitude or altitude) and

3. if pH values are low.

The low rate of decomposition is often reflected in a low rate of 'soil respiration' in other words consumption of oxygen by the peat.

TABLE 4.4
SOIL RESPIRATION RATES AT VARIOUS SITES (μ litre O_2/g/h)

Limestone grassland at high altitude 556m (UK)[15]	150
Mixed *Eriophorum/Calluna* blanket bog high alt. 550m (UK)[15]	33–36
Podsol profile[16]	473
Bare, redistributed peat[15] high alt. 564m (UK)	1

Table 4.4 gives some soil respiration figures which illustrate these points. Soils at similar altitudes and latitudes show higher oxygen consumption if they are well aerated and at a higher pH (e.g. limestone grassland). Soils from lower altitudes tend to have higher oxygen consumption, i.e. higher rates of microbial activity.

Latter, Cragg and Heal[15] have found that this diminution in microbial activity with increased wetness and lowered pH is associated with several changes in the soil microflora.

1. Total numbers of bacteria are fewer in peat sites than in limestone grassland at the same altitude. Values of $16–79 \times 10^8$/cm³ for the grassland and $14–35 \times 10^8$/cm³ for the blanket peat were obtained. The variation in values was dependent upon season.

2. Fungi were difficult to determine because many of the hyphae found in the peat site could have been dead and a component of the peat itself rather than actively decomposing it. They attempted to separate living hyphae by staining and on this basis estimated the total length of hyphae as 160–580m/cm³ in the limestone grassland compared with 15–180m/cm³ in the blanket peat.

3. The ratio of bacteria : length of fungal mycelium decreased from 1 : 300 in the limestone grassland to 1 : 1300 in the peat. Thus the fungal component of the decomposer system becomes more prominent at low pH.

4. Bacteria involved in the nitrogen cycle, both aerobic nitrogen fixing bacteria and nitrifying bacteria (involved in the oxidation of NH_4^+ to NO_3^-) were virtually absent from the peat. This is of considerable importance when we consider the nitrogen balance of the system, for not only is there a lack of nitrogen

entering the system as a result, but also the nitrogen present is unlikely to be recycled in the absence of nitrifying agents.

Thus low pH and waterlogged conditions have a marked effect upon the microbial element of the decomposer food chain, but technical difficulties, such as the separation of living and dead mycelium and the extraction of bacteria from within dead cells for dilution counting, make quantitative data very difficult to obtain. Few fungi are able to exist anaerobically, apart from yeasts (which are present in acid peats in some quantity[15]), which leads one to expect that the bulk of the mycelium thrives in the surface layers of peat, which are not subject to constant waterlogging. It may well be that such mycelial growth occurs during drier periods when water tables are lowered and conditions are aerobic. However, there are no data available to demonstrate this conclusively. The predominance of fungi rather than bacteria in bog peats is therefore probably associated with the acid conditions rather than waterlogged ones.

The presence of an aerobic layer at the surface of bogs and an anaerobic zone below this is easily demonstrated by leaving a copper wire inserted into the peat[17]. The upper portion of the wire (perhaps 10—20 cm) is unaffected, but the lower part becomes blackened by the formation of a sulphide deposit on its surface. This is caused by the presence of hydrogen sulphide produced by obligately anaerobic organisms in the deeper parts of the peat. One such group of organisms is the genus *Desulphovibrio.*

Anaerobic decomposers such as *Desulphovibrio* require specialised respiratory systems. Some, such as the yeasts, utilise a fermentation reaction in the absence of oxygen and incompletely oxidise the organic substrate. *Desulphovibrio* makes use of oxygen in a combined form with sulphur, either sulphate or sulphite ions[18]. An example of the kind of oxidation — reduction reaction possible is provided by the following summary equation.

$$CH_3 . CO.COOH + SO_4'' \longrightarrow 4 CO_2 + S'' + 4 CH_3 . COOH$$

Here an organic substrate, pyruvate, is completely oxidised to carbon dioxide in the absence of aerobic oxygen. It is by mechanisms such as these that some microbes, mainly bacteria, yeasts and a few specialised mycelium producing fungi, manage to survive and metabolise in an anaerobic, waterlogged medium.

The next question of importance is where does decomposition proceed most rapidly in a peat profile. R.S. Clymo[19] has performed some experiments upon the breakdown rate of *Sphagnum* at various depths in peat which help to answer this problem. He took dried samples of *Sphagnum* and placed them in nylon bags with a mesh of 1.0 mm. These he buried at various depths in two *Sphagnum* mires which differed greatly in altitude and climate, one at Moor House (575m) in northwest England and the other at Thursley Common (30m) in southern England.

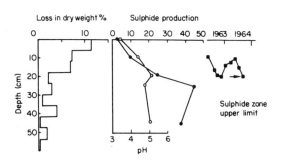

Figure 4.6. Depth at Thursley bog related to percentage loss in dry weight of Sphagnum papillosumı *(left). Upper limit of sulphide at various times of year (■), pH at 31 August (○) and H₂S production in arbitrary units after 13 days in enrichment culture (●). The arrow shows the upper level of sulphide at the time when the samples for pH and microbiological activity were taken. (J. Ecol. 53, 753 (1965) Figure 3)*

Figure 4.6 shows the results for the Thursley site after 103 days. It can be seen from this histogram that the greatest losses in dry weight occurred at the surface of the mire. Losses become gradually smaller down to a depth of 20 cm after which they fluctuated around a fairly low level (c. 2.5% dry weight loss). Also given for comparison are the fluctuation in the upper limit of sulphide deposition on a copper wire over the course of a year, the pH on a single date at various levels, and the activity of *Desulphovibrio*, gauged by the production of H_2S from an enrichment culture of the peat at various depths collected under anaerobic, sterile conditions. H_2S production increases down the profile to a maximum at about 25 cm. Sulphide deposition on a wire fluctuates through the year, but its level at the time of sampling for H_2S (arrowed) is above the zone of maximum H_2S production. Although the fluctuations in the upper limit of the 'sulphide zone' are almost certainly connected with the water table, the latter fluctuates more rapidly and by larger amounts than does the upper limit of the sulphide zone.

These experiments of Clymo demonstrate that the bulk of the

100

decomposition, of *Sphagnum* at least, occurs in the aerobic layer above the anaerobic sulphide zone. Once within the zone, the rate of decomposition is probably less than a fifth the rate at the peat surface. Results from Moor House were consistently lower than those at Thursley, which probably reflects the lower temperatures and therefore the lower rates of microbial metabolism at higher altitudes.

We can summarise the results of these and other experiments on decomposition in mires as follows:

1. Decomposition rate varies with different species of *Sphagnum*, e.g. *Sphagnum papillosum* decomposes at only about half the rate of *S. cuspidatum*[19].

2. The rate of decomposition diminishes as one passes deeper into the peat, in part due to the anaerobic, reducing conditions under which relatively few decomposer organisms can function.

3. Different compounds are metabolised at different rates by decomposer organisms. The more easily metabolised compounds will be used up most rapidly, leaving less palatable substances to be degraded more slowly. This implies that decomposition rate is rapid in initial stages, but becomes slower as time proceeds[20, 21].

4. The overall rate of peat accumulation will depend upon the rate at which material produced at the surface enters the sulphide zone, where decomposition becomes considerably slower. This will be a function of two main factors, the rate of primary production at the surface and the height of the water table, i.e. the distance between the point of production and the sulphide zone. In practice these two factors are often interrelated, since the height of water table is of major importance in controlling rates of *Sphagnum* productivity; however this is not necessarily always the case. This point will be raised once again when we consider the interpretation of undecomposed bands of *Sphagnum* in peat profiles (see Chapter 6).

Decomposer Animals

It would be wrong to give the impression that microbial organisms are the only ones concerned in the decomposition process. Animals are also very important in decomposition within peatland habitats[23, 24]. Macfadyen[24] has compared the activity of the soil fauna of several habitats in terms of their respiration in the course of a year. Table 4.5 shows the respiration rates of various groups of soil animals in peat from *Juncus squarrosus* moor and in litter from an oak wood.

From these data it can be seen that the importance of fauna in decomposition is similar in both sites, being rather greater in the

TABLE 4.5
RESPIRATION OF SOIL ANIMALS FROM A *JUNCUS* MOOR AND
AN OAK WOOD IN kcal/m^2/annum.

Juncus moor		*Oak woodland*	
Herbivores	145	Herbivores	118
Large Decomposers	6	Large Decomposers	129
Small Decomposers	293	Small Decomposers	114
Predators	13	Predators	20
Total	457	Total	381

moorland. The major difference between the sites is in the relative importance of large and small decomposer organisms. In the moorland situation there is a strong preponderance of small decomposer animals over larger ones which is not apparent in woodland. Table 4.6 gives a breakdown of respiration figures into taxonomic groupings. From this it can be seen that there is an absence of Isopoda and Diplopoda amongst the large decomposer group of moorland peats which accounts for this difference between sites.

TABLE 4.6
BREAKDOWN OF RESPIRATION FIGURES FOR MOORLAND SOILS FAUNA
GIVEN IN TABLE 4.5 (FROM CRAGG[23]) IN kcal/m^2/annum.

Herbivores	Nematodes	13·7
	Diptera	131·3
Large Decomposers	Lumbricids	5·5
Small Decomposers	Nematodes	6·8
	Enchytraeids	269·0
	Oribatids	13·0
	Collembola	4·1
Predators	Parasitids	13·0

The species composition of decomposer communities varies between different microhabitats as environmental factors vary. For example Nematodes become more abundant where there is a higher mineral content in the peat, whereas Oribatids and Collembola are more frequent in organic peats where they feed upon fungi[24]. Within the Collembola, Hale[25] and others[26] have shown that different species become important in different situations on the mire surface. Hale studied a secondary succession in a blanket mire area where erosion had occurred and regeneration was active, He demonstrated a vegetational succession following peat erosion which can be represented as follows:

Bare peat $\longrightarrow$ Invasion of surface algae $\longrightarrow$ *Eriophorum angustifolium*

$\longrightarrow$ *E. vaginatum* $\longrightarrow$ *Calluna* and
tussocks   mixed moor

The bare peat had no Collembola, but once algae had invaded a suitable microhabitat for Collembola was produced. A single species, *Isotoma antennalis*, is able to survive beneath the algal mats. Once tussocky *E. vaginatum* has invaded, the habitat becomes much more diverse, offering opportunity for a variety of animals to make a living. A variety of Collembola are able to live in this type of vegetation; in effect a hydrophilous fauna has been replaced by a mesophilous one. Should erosion result in the isolation of portions of the peat in the form of 'hags', drying of the mire surface reduces the diversity of the collembolan fauna once again.

Undoubtedly effects of this kind could be demonstrated in other groups of decomposter animals also, but few data are yet available.

Estimation of productivity in these decomposer animals can be very difficult, especially in groups such as the Enchytraeids, where fragmentation is a means of reproduction and therefore mortality is difficult to estimate. Standen[27] has estimated a productivity of about 11.5 g/m²/annum for Pennine blanket peat where the standing crop is 68 g/m² (this is equivalent to 80 000 individuals per m²).

Herbivores

Table 4.6 shows that the bulk of the herbivore trophic level in moorland peats is occupied by Diptera larvae, together with herbivorous Nematodes. Mites are often abundant also. Quantitative data are scarce, but it is probably generally true that invertebrate herbivores are more important than vertebrates in peatland situations. Nevertheless, vertebrate herbivores, particularly birds, may be conspicuous members of the peatland fauna.

The early, rheotrophic stages in peatland succession are often more productive than the later ombrotrophic stages and they also produce a vegetation which is richer in the nutrients necessary for vertebrate life and growth, particularly calcium and magnesium for skeletal structures. It is not surprising, therefore, that these early seral stages bear a more dense and a more diverse vertebrate fauna. A reed-swamp in Europe, for example, may contain a variety of herbivorous and omnivorous ducks (e.g. mallard, *Anas platyrhynchos*, teal, *A. crecca* and wigeon, *A. penelope*) plus herbivorous mammals (e.g. water shrew, *Neomys fodiens* and water vole, *Arvicola amphibius*). In addition such reedswamp may contain insectivorous birds such as reed warbler, *Acrocephalus scirpaceus* and sedge warbler, *A. schoenobaenus* and predators such as marsh harrier, *Circus aeruginosus,* forming a fourth trophic level.

Ombrotrophic mires contain a less diverse vertebrate fauna, although some northern mires of this type are occupied by certain specialised species, e.g. greenshank, *Tringa nebularia* and crane, *Grus grus.*

Mires in temperate regions may provide a seasonal source of food for migratory species, e.g. the *Acrocephalus* species mentioned above which are summer visitors, or Greenland whitefronted geese, *Anser albifrons*, which visit ombrotrophic mires in western Europe during winter where they feed upon the seeds of *Rhyncospora alba,* the white-beaked sedge.

In the United States there is a controlled cropping of waterfowl for sport and human consumption. This necessitates the management of favoured wetland areas to maintain high productivity and nutrient availability. Some wetlands are drained, ploughed, kept dry for a year and then reflooded, which has the effect of checking vigorous, invasive species such as *Phragmites* and *Salix* and allowing a certain degree of aeration and decomposition, resulting in nutrient release from surface peat layers. In effect the management practice retains an early successional stage which favours the prey species.

PEAT ACCUMULATION — RATES OF PEAT FORMATION

We have seen how anaerobic conditions in peatlands curtail the activity of decomposer organisms and restricts their distribution in any quantity to an aerated layer above the sulphide zone. The fact that decomposition rate fails to keep pace with productivity results in peat formation, the rate of which will be dependent upon the ratio of these two processes. It might be expected, therefore, that just as productivity varies between different types of vegetation, so will rates of peat formation.

A simple equation to illustrate this[22] is:

$$\frac{dX}{dt} = L - kX$$

where X = amount of accumulation, L = rate of 'litter' fall, and k = fractional rate of loss. This oversimplifies the situation since it assumes a constant rate of aeration and of loss, which is far from the natural situation where climate season, water table and nutrient supply may all be expected to affect these rates. However, even in this simple model it can be seen that L and k will vary in different vegetation types.

Peat accumulation in any system is a slow process; an average figure, for example, would be of the order of between 20 and 80 cm in 1000 years[28]. The slowness of this process makes it very difficult to measure precisely. One of the most effective means of estimating its rate is by obtaining dates for specific layers in the stratigraphy of peat profiles and thus calculating rates of peat buildup. There are, however, certain disadvantages in this method.

1. Dating is neither simple nor very accurate. Radiocarbon dating is probably the best available but may have wide errors, especially if we are dealing with peats penetrated by roots from above. Pollen analysis is ultimately dependent upon absolute scales such as radiocarbon for its precision and even then it has yet to be demonstrated that 'pollen zones' are synchronous throughout the country (see Chapter 7).

2. Compaction of peat occurs as new material is laid down above. One would expect lower layers to be more tightly compressed than upper ones.

3. The rates of formation may be expected to vary with climate and since climate is in a constant state of flux it is invalid to compare peat accretion rates during different periods in the past.

Bearing these problems in mind it is nevertheless interesting to look at some figures which have been collected from a variety of sources by Walker[28]. These figures show the rate of peat formation for swamp, fen and bog vegetation at a variety of British and Irish sites for various periods in the past (see Table 4.7). A number of surprising features

TABLE 4.7
AVERAGE RATES OF PEAT FORMATION IN BOGS AND FENS, (cm/100 yr).
FIGURES IN BRACKETS ARE NUMBER OF SAMPLES.
(MODIFIED FROM WALKER, 1970)[28].

7800-7000 BC	100 (1)	93 (1)
7000-5400 BC	86 (3)	103 (2)
5400-3000 BC	— (0)	46 (5)
3000- 500 BC	70 (1)	64 (14)
500 BC-500 AD	— (0)	54·(4)
500 AD +	— (0)	18 (1)

emerge from these figures. In the first place, where it is possible to compare directly the rates of peat accretion under bog and fen conditions, there would seem to be very little difference between them. In fact, further data of Walker's demonstrate that the rates are not very different from those of organic nekron muds accumulated in lakes with floating aquatic plants at the same periods. It would certainly be unwise for us to postulate, therefore, any general difference in the rates of peat formation under fen and bog vegetation types.

A further interesting point, though one of dubious statistical significance is the variation in peat formation at different periods in the past. These do not appear to agree with what we know of climatic conditions during those times. For example the period 7000 − 5400 BC is normally regarded as having been drier than the period 5400 − 3000 BC, yet rates of bog formation are far greater in the former. This may be in part due to the initiation of new bogs in the later period at sites where bog growth would not have been possible during the earlier one. However, this does not explain all of the figures. We shall return to this point later.

Cameron[29] has accumulated some data on peat formation in North America. She quotes values of bog growth of the order of 100 − 200 cm/1000 years, which are rather higher than the average British values. These apply to bogs in Pennsylvania and Canada. An interesting figure for the rate of accretion in saw grass peat in the Everglades of Florida is about 130 cm/1000 years[30].

NUTRIENTS IN PEATLANDS

Having looked in some detail at the way in which energy moves through the peatland ecosystem and is eventually partially stored in these ecosystems, we can now turn our attention to nutrient cycling, a subject which was outlined at the beginning of this chapter. There we discussed the major routes which nutrients take within the ecosystem (Figure 4.3). We shall now look in greater detail at the relative importance of these nutrient reservoirs and patterns of movement.

It has long been recognised that the ionic composition of wetlands varies considerably and that such variations are usually accompanied by floristic changes in the surface vegetation, e.g. the work of Sjörs[31] (see Chapter 3). Table 4.8 demonstrates the variation in water chemistry possible in a single mire, Wyburnbury Moss, Cheshire, only c.15 ha. in area[32]. We shall be considering these relationships in later chapters. The origins of these ionic components are twofold, the weathering of surrounding rocks and the leaching of local soils, together with the precipitation from the air, including dust, wind transported

TABLE 4.8
WATER CHEMISTRY AND ASSOCIATED VEGETATION AT
WYBURNBURY MOSS, CHESHIRE (FROM POORE AND
WALKER, 1959)[32]. VALUES IN p.p.m.

	Na	K	Ca	Fe	P_2O_5	Cl	Mg
Sphagnum lawn	8·60	5·45	3·22	0·75	0·046	23·10	4·64
Eriophorum augustifolium	12·63	4·63	8·11	0·73	0·007	25·80	2·50
Phragmites swamp	26·25	17·18	78·44	0·20	0·016	52·00	30·82
Carex paniculata swamp	31·50	7·0	73·44	0·24	0·003	74·00	37·20

minerals and soil particles, and ions in aerosol form derived from the sea.

The relative importance of these two sources of ions varies with hydrology, geology and factors affecting aerial transport of ions, such as proximity to the sea. Although there are abundant data relating to the chemical constitution of mire waters at particular points in time, there are currently no full data concerning the quantity of nutrients entering a mire ecosystem from drainage water during the course of a year, nor for that matter data on nutrients leaving mires. There is, however, an increasing quantity of information upon nutrient input into various ecosystems by precipitation. Much of these data have been collated by Gore[33] and some selected figures are given in Table 4.9 (see also Chapter 3).

TABLE 4.9
ANNUAL NUTRIENT INPUT (kg/ha) BY RAINWATER AT VARIOUS SITES

Site	Annual rainfall (cm)	Inorganic N	P	Na	K	Ca	Mg
Lerwick (Shetland Isles)[34]	57·3	2·10	—	133·00	5·52	6·70	19·20
Lancashire (UK)[35]	161·7	6·28	0·43	35·34	2·96	7·30	4·63
Pennines (UK)[33]	186·1	6·89	0·27	32·14	2·27	9·53	4·48
Kent (UK)[36]	84·0	—	<0·4	19·30	2·80	10·70	<4·20
Hubbard Brook (USA)[37]	129·0	—	—	1·5	1·40	2·60	0·70

The effect of proximity to the sea is clearly seen in the Lerwick figures, where sodium attains very high values. The figures from

107

Hubbard Brook are from a site on the northeastern side of the United States and here there is far less nutrient input from rainfall than at any of the British stations.

Gore has demonstrated that there are significant differences for nutrient input figures between years and that these differences are associated with variations in the precipitation. One might expect that the ratios of nutrients in rainwater will be similar to those found in sea water if this is indeed the major source of aerial nutrients. This is reasonably true of an oceanic site such as Lerwick, where the ratio of Ca : Mg (0.21) is similar to that found in seawater (0.196), however, it is not true of more inland sites, e.g. 3.7 for Hubbard Brook. This could be due to a number of factors, but the most likely one is the use of agricultural lime and fertilizers which probably contribute a considerable quantity of calcium to the airborne dust.

This supply of nutrients is particularly important to mires which receive no drainage water from surrounding land (ombrotrophic bogs) and, when coupled with various mechanisms for nutrient conservation in the vegetation, it is adequate to account for continued bog growth. Nitrogen is a major component of plant and animal tissues which is accumulated in peat deposits and therefore is needed in constant supply at the surface. Jörgensen (1927)[38] calculated the average annual nitrogen accumulation in peat in three raised bogs in Denmark over the last 2500 years as 6.524 kg/ha. A recent study of nutrients in rainfall in that area (Jensen, 1962)[39] gives a figure for nitrogen of 6.9 kg/ha/annum which appears to be adequate to account for continued peat growth.

Some work has been done on bogs in Minnesota[40] which receive insoluble minerals by aerial transport from the prairies to the west. From radiocarbon dates it can be calculated that these minerals have accumulated at an average rate of 0.29 kg/ha/annum over the last 2250 years. Much of this material is over 2μ in size and consists largely of opal, quartz and feldspars. Most of the opal is in the form of phytoliths, which are derived primarily from grasses and which make up 2 — 5% of the surface horizon of mineral soils developed under prairie vegetation. Although this insoluble matter is unlikely to be an important source of nutrients for the bog, one must assume that much soluble material accompanied it and this could have represented a considerable source of nutrient input. This may apply to many bogs developing in continental areas or in the vicinity of grasslands.

Nutrients entering an ombrotrophic mire via precipitation are likely either to become attached to the peat by cation exchange or to be lost to the system by surface runoff of waters. Under conditions of high precipitation, where such mires usually develop, this could present a serious loss to the system. Once attached to peat the nutrients may take one of four courses:

1. to be leached out and lost,
2. to remain attached to the peat and be incorporated into the deposit,
3. to be released by exchange or microbial action, or fire and to be absorbed by plant roots, or
4. to remain attached to the peat and be lost by erosion.

The precise quantity of nutrients present in peat at any given time is very difficult to determine because its value varies according to the method of analysis used, particularly the agent used for leaching[41]. It is even more difficult to know how much of the nutrient present in the peat is available to the plant. Some of the material recovered by ashing peat would be bound into the organic matter and would not be available to plants until released by microbial action. A possible approach is to analyse the plant material and determine how much of a particular nutrient is being absorbed. Using this method on *Eriophorum vaginatum* blanket bog in Wales, Goodman and Perkins[42] determined that of the three elements N, P and K which are in short supply in such situations, potassium is ultimately limiting to the growth of *Eriophorum.*

In general, the vegetation of an ecosystem which is low in nutrient capital (such as ombrotrophic mire) will be nondemanding in nutrient requirements and therefore low in nutrient content. The latter will, of course, vary seasonally with factors such as growth rates, fruit production and litter fall. This seasonal variation is found also in swamp plants under eutrophic conditions (see Figure 4.7). In an experiment by Boyd[43], *Typha latifolia* absorbed phosphorus at its highest rate at the end of April which corresponds with the commencement of spring growth. Flowering and fruiting occurred during June and July and nitrogen, phosphorus and magnesium were concentrated in the seed heads. The absorption of these nutrients during the period is insufficient to account for the high concentrations in fruits, which must have derived them by translocation at the expense of other parts of the plant.

Thus nutrient movements occur within the plant itself and some of these are of critical importance for the nutrient budget of a bog system. An example is the way in which many nutrients in *Eriophorum* communities are translocated back to the perennating organ prior to litter fall in the autumn. In this way also nutrients in seeds provide a readily available resource for seedling establishment.

Burning of vegetation accelerates the movement of nutrients in an ecosystem, and is of particular importance in moorland situations. Allen[44] has calculated that in a *Calluna* dominated ecosystem with a

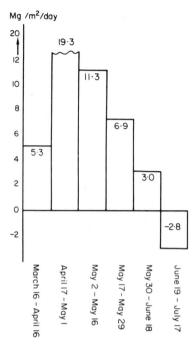

Figure 4.7. Rate of uptake of P by Typha latifolia from March to July[43]
(mg/m²/day)

standing crop of 1 kg/m², 0.1 g/m² of potassium may be lost during
burning, both in smoke and as a result of the increased leaching rate.
The latter is a consequence of the flushing of nutrients into the surface
peat layers and the increased run off resulting from diminished transpiration. Such a loss could represent almost a half of the total annual
input of potassium by precipitation in an area such as the Pennines
where 0.227 g/m² enters the system in this way[33]. Thus fire can
accentuate problems of low nutrient levels on ombrotrophic mires.

Very little data are currently available on the rates at which nutrients
are released from litter by microbial activity, apart from the work by
Latter and Cragg on *Juncus squarrosus*[17] and Frankland[45] on *Pteridium
aquilinum*. The former demonstrated that 50% of total inorganic ions
in *Juncus* leaves were lost in the first five months. The order of loss
of these ions was

$$K > P > Mg > Ca$$

110

Once again it is potassium which is most rapidly released into the environment and which is therefore in danger of being leached. On the other hand, its rapid release means that little potassium will remain in the organic matter once it reaches (or is reached by) the sulphide zone where decomposition rate diminishes.

There are, then, three processes which result in the retention of certain nutrients in the living plants on upper layers of peat. These are:

1. return of nutrients to perennating organs
2. penetration of deeper peat zones by roots and the transport of nutrients to the surface, and
3. rapid differential release of certain nutrients by microbial activity in the upper peat layers.

The effects of these processes can be clearly demonstrated by the study of the chemistry of peat profiles. For example, Table 3.11 shows data from a *Sphagnum fuscum* hummock from Westmorland, England[12]. There is a very distinct concentration of all the ions measured in the top 3 cm of peat, which contains the living material.

Stewart and Robertson[46] examined the chemical status of an exposed peat face, 1 m in depth, in Scottish blanket bog. Although phosphorus, potassium and calcium were most abundant in the upper few centimetres, other ions, e.g. Mg^{++}, Na^+, SO_3'', show peaks at lower points in the profile. The authors associate these with differing vegetational composition of the peat.

Chapman[47] studied the chemical profile of a mire nearly 5 m in depth at Coom Rigg, Northumberland. The upper 4 m of this profile are of *Sphagnum/Eriophorum* peat of varying degrees of humification. Even within this uniform peat he demonstrates considerable peaks of certain elements, particularly aluminium and silica. These he attributes to deposition on the contemporary bog surface due to wind erosion, similar to that shown by Finney and Farnham in Minnesota[40]. He shows that these deposition periods correspond with pollen indications of human interference with vegetation in the area, the clearance of woodland leading to grassland production and the consequent dissemination of silica phytoliths.

Chapman also lays stress upon the ratio of Ca : Mg in his profiles. He postulates that when it falls below a value of 1.0 the nutrient regime of the mire has passed from rheotrophic to ombrotrophic. This is based upon the assumption that the precipitation will contain calcium and magnesium in a similar ratio to that of seawater. We have seen earlier in this chapter that this is not the case at the present day, but it is possible that it was so before man spread lime in large

111

quantities. Chapman shows a close correlation between changes in this ratio and changes in the peat stratigraphy which one might associate with a rheotrophic to ombrotrophic transition, e.g. *Phragmites* ⟶ *Sphagnum/Eriophorum*. It is perhaps surprising that such changes are so clearly demonstrable in a peat profile when one considers how nutrients are selectively carried upwards with the peat surface as the deposit grows.

Overall Nutrient Budgets

We have traced a number of courses which nutrients may take once within an ecosystem; we can now look at overall gains and losses to the system and assess its nutrient budget.

To obtain such figures it is necessary to record both nutrient input by precipitation for a system and the output in erosion and as dissolved matter in drainage water. Such a study can best be carried out in a region where the geological substratum is impervious so that all losses are carried by surface stream water[48]. Stream flow rates can then be monitored by the installation of a V-notch weir and the nutrient content of the stream waters can be analysed as frequently as is necessary. From these data, together with any other likely input or output sources, the overall nutrient budget for a watershed area can be established.

Very few such complete studies have as yet been undertaken, but Table 4.10 gives figures for a study in blanket mire in the Pennines and

TABLE 4.10
NUTRIENT BALANCE SHEET FOR AN AREA OF PENNINE MOORLAND (kg/ha/annum). AFTER CRISP (1966)[49]

	Na	K	Ca	P	N
Input by precipitation	25·540	3·070	8·980	0·690	8·200
Output					
1. Sale of sheep	0·002	0·005	0·019	0·012	0·053
2. Dissolved matter in stream	45·270	8·970	53·810	0·39	2·940
3. Drift of fauna in stream	0·001	0·005	0·001	0·005	0·057
4. Erosion of peat in stream	0·280	2·060	4·830	0·450	14·630
Total Output	45·550	11·040	58·660	0·860	17·680
Net Loss	20·010	7·970	49·680	0·150	9·480

Table 4.11 provides figures for comparison from a woodland ecosystem in the United States. The Pennine ecosystem consists of 83 hectares of blanket peat fed by springs from peat channels and from some high level limestone rocks. It lies at an altitude of 563 m and 11% of the catchment area consists of actively eroding peat. The woodland eco-

system is situated in New Hampshire in the northeastern United States. It is dominated by hardwoods, largely *Acer saccharum, Fagus grandifolia* and *Betula allegheniensis* and it lies at an altitude of 245 m. It is underlain by impervious till and gneiss and is 13 hectares in area.

The differences in nutrient content of precipitation have already been discussed in this chapter. The higher values for the Pennine area reflect not only its more maritime position but also its higher overall rainfall (207 cm p.a. compared with 129 cm p.a. in the New Hampshire site).

The situation in the moorland area is slightly complicated by the fact that sheep are grazed and harvested from the area. Pearsall[51] initially pointed out that the harvesting of sheep from blanket bog could represent a serious drain upon the nutrient resources fo the habitat. The flesh, wool and hide is rich in nitrogen, together with some sulphur and phosphorus and the bone material is largely calcium phosphate. Over a period of decades, or even centuries, one might expect this harvesting to cause depletion of these elements. The Pennine watershed study was in part designed to determine the relative losses of nutrients by this means.

The findings of the study, rather surprisingly, indicate that the nutrient losses due to sheep harvesting are extremely low, of the same order as those due to the drift of fauna (mainly arthropods) in the stream. One cannot therefore consider the harvesting of sheep as a major source of nutrient depletion.

The erosion of peat, however, does represent a serious loss. In the case of potassium, calcium and phosphorus, over 50% of the annual input by precipitation is lost in this way. Nitrogen losses in peat erosion are even more serious, considerably exceeding the precipitation input.

These losses in eroded material are considerably greater than the particulate losses in the woodland ecosystem (Table 4.11), where the total erosion losses are of the order of 10 — 20% of the precipitation input. Peat erosion, therefore, must be considered as a serious loss of nutrient capital for upland blanket bog. There are two factors, however, which need to be considered in the assessment of the seriousness of this process. In the first place, much of the nutrient content of the peat will be bound up in undecomposed material in a situation where release is unlikely. Thus much peat can be regarded as reservoirs of unavailable nutrient material and therefore its loss is unlikely to affect the surface vegetation. In fact it may allow the growth of a more nutrient demanding vegetation type by exposing mineral soil once again. Secondly, the figures for both of the sites do not take account of the rate of

113

TABLE 4.11
NUTRIENT BUDGET FOR A FOREST ECOSYSTEM IN THE NORTHEAST
UNITED STATES (kg/ha/annum). FROM BORMANN, *ET AL*[50, 37]

	Na	K	Ca	N
Input	1·50	1·40	2·60	—
Output				
1. Organic particulate matter in stream	0·00	0·01	0·07	0·12
2. Inorganic particulate matter in stream	0·19	0·32	0·18	—
3. Dissolved matter in stream	6·55	1·50	9·85	1·90
Total Loss	6·74	1·83	10·10	2·02
Net Loss	5·24	0·43	7·50	—

weathering of the parent material, which may well comprise an important input for nutrients, especially in the case of the woodland. If these quantities were known, losses in peat erosion might appear less serious. However, the net nitrogen losses are still likely to be excessive, despite lack of data on microbial nitrogen fixation rates at these sites.

Weathering rates of parent material must also be considered when interpreting the losses as dissolved matter. For example, the very high calcium losses in the Pennine system are undoubtedly due to the effect of limestone weathering in a part of the catchment, which is flushing directly into the stream. These rocks, however, are unlikely to be contributing greatly to the dissolved losses of other elements. In their woodland study in New Hampshire, Bormann and Likens[50] assumed that the biota and soils of the ecosystem were in dynamic equilibrium and that therefore the chemical decomposition rate of underlying bedrock and till was adequate to compensate for other losses. One cannot make such an assumption in the case of the blanket bog. Undoubtedly weathering is contributing much to the budget, but there remains the possibility that there is an overall net loss of nutrients to the system, particularly to that portion of the system effectively insulated from weathering products by a layer of peat. If this is so it will be reflected in vegetational change in an ombrotrophic direction.

The data presented in this chapter illustrate the chief characteristics of mire ecosystems and show how these complex biotic systems differ from terrestrial communities. All of their peculiar attributes can ultimately be traced to the wetness of the abiotic template condition and the resulting accretion of the complex organic material we call peat. The precise composition of this substance will be the subject of Chapters 6 and 7, but first we shall look in more detail at some of the problems facing organisms which dwell in the peatland environment.

REFERENCES

1. BOLIN, B. 'The carbon cycle.' *Scientific American,* **223,** (3), 125 (1970).
2. ECKARDT, F.E. (Ed.). 'Functioning of terrestrial ecosystems at the primary production level.' *UNESCO Symposium at Copenhagen, Paris* (1968).
3. ECKARDT, F.E. (Ed.). 'Methodology of plant ecophysiology.' *UNESCO Symposium at Montpellier, Paris* (1965).
4. WOODWELL, G.M. and WHITTAKER, R.H. 'Primary production in terrestrial ecosystems.' *Am. Zoologist.* **8,.**19 (1968).
5. FIALA, K., DYKYJOVA, D., KVET, J. and SVOBODA, J. 'Methods of assessing rhizophere and root production in reed bed stands.' In *Methods of productivity studies in root systems and rhizosphere organisms.* USSR Academy of Sciences, Leningrad, 36 (1968).
6. WESTLAKE, D.F. 'Methods used to determine the annual production of reedswamp plants with extensive rhizomes.' In *Methods of productivity studies in root systems and rhizosphere organisms.* USSR Academy of Sciences, Leningrad, 226 (1968).
7. RODIN, L.E. and BASILEVICH, N.I. 'World distribution of plant biomass.' In *Functioning of terrestrial ecosystems of the primary production level.* Ed. F.E. ECKARDT, UNECSO, Paris (1968).
8. WESTLAKE, D.F. 'Comparisons of plant productivity.' *Biol. Rev.* **38,** 385 (1963).
9. WALKER, J.M. and WAYGOOD, E.F. 'Ecology of *Phragmites communis,* I. Photosynthesis of a single shoot *in situ.*' *Can. J. Bot.* **46,** 549 (1968).
10. CLYMO, R.S. 'The growth of *Sphagnum:* methods of measurement.' *J. Ecol.* **58,** 13 (1970).
11. OVERBECK, F. and HAPPACH, H. 'Uber das Wachstum und den Wasserhaushalt einiger Hochmoorsphagnen.' *Flora, Jena,* **144,** 335 (1956).
12. BELLAMY, D.J. and RIELEY, J. 'Some ecological statistics of a miniature bog.' *Oikos,* **18,** 33 (1967).
13. TURNER, J. 'The anthropogenic factor in vegetational history. I. Tregaron and Whixal Mosses.' *New Phytol.* **63,** 73 (1964).
14. FORREST, G.I. 'Structure and production of North Pennine blanket bog vegetation.' *J. Ecol.* **59,** 453 (1971).
15. LATTER, P.M., CRAGG, J.B. and HEAL, O.W. 'Comparative studies on the microbiology of four moorland soils in the North Pennines.' *J. Ecol.* **55,** 445 (1967).
16. BURGES, A. 'Some problems in soil microbiology.' *Trans. Br. mycol. Soc.* **46,** 1 (1963).
17. LATTER, P.M. and CRAGG, J.B. 'The decomposition of *Juncus squarrosus* leaves and microbiological changes in the profile of a *Juncus* moor.' *J. Ecol.* **55,** 465 (1967).
18. BENDA, I. 'Mikrobiologische untersuchungen uber das auftreten, von schavefelwasserstoff in den anaeroben zonen des hochmoores.' *Arch. Mikrobiol.* **27,** 337 (1957).
19. CLYMO, R.S. 'Experiments on the breakdown of *Sphagnum* in two bogs.' *J. Ecol.* **53,** 747 (1965).
20. WAKSMAN, S.A. and STEVENS, K.R. 'Contributions to the chemical composition of peat. V. The role of micro-organisms in peat formation and decomposition.' *Soil Sci.* **27,** 271 (1929).
21. THEANDER, O. 'Studies on *Sphagnum* peat. 3. A quantitative study of the

carbohydrate constituents of *Sphagnum* mosses and *Sphagnum* peat.' *Acta chem. Scand.* **8**, 989 (1954).

22. OLSON, J.S. 'Energy storage and the balance of producers and decomposers in ecological systems.' *Ecology,* **44,** 322 (1963).
23. CRAGG, J.B. 'Some aspects of the ecology of ·moorland animals.' *J. Anim. Ecol.* **30,** 205 (1961).
24. MACFADYEN, A. 'The contribution of the microfauna to total soil metabolism.' In *Soil Organisms,* Ed. DOEKSEN, J. and VAN DER DRIFT, J. Amsterdam, 3 (1963).
25. HALE, W.G. (1963). 'The Collembola of eroding blanket bog.' In *Soil Organisms.* Ed. DOEKSEN, J. and VAN DER DRIFT, J. Amsterdam, 406 (1963).
26. MURPHY, D.H. 'Long term changes in Collembolan populations with special reference to moorland soils. In *'Soil Zoology.'* Ed. KEVAN, London, 157 (1955).
27. STANDEN, U. 'The production of moorland Enchytraids.' *British Ecological Society Winter Meeting, York* (1971).
28. WALKER, D. 'Direction and rate in some British post-glacial hydroseres.' In *Studies in the Vegetational History of the British Isles.* Ed. WALKER, D. and WEST, R.G. Cambridge, 117 (1970).
29. CAMERON, C.C. 'Peat deposits of northeastern Pennsylvania.' *U.S. Geol. Survey Bull.* 1317. A. 1 (1970).
30. DAVIS, J.H. 'The peat deposits of Florida, their occurrence, development and uses.' *Florida Geol. Survey Bull.* **30,** 1 (1946).
31. SJÖRS, H. 'On the relation between vegetation and electrolytes in north Swedish mire waters. *Oikos,* **2,** 241 (1950).
32. POORE, M.E.D. and WALKER, D. 'Wyburnbury Moss, Cheshire.' *Mem. Proc. Manchester Lit. Phil. Soc.* **101,** 72 (1959).
33. GORE, A.J.P. 'The supply of six elements by rain to an upland peat area.' *J. Ecol.* **56,** 483 (1968).
34. EGNER, H. and ERIKSSON, E. 'Current data on the chemical composition of air and precipitation.' *Tellus,* 10-12 (1958-60).
35. CARLISLE, A., BROWN, A.H.F. and WHITE, E.J. 'The organic matter and nutrient elements in the precipitation beneath a sessile oak *(Quercus petraea)* Canopy.' *J. Ecol.* **54,** 87 (1966).
36. MADGWICK, H.A.I. and OVINGTON, J.D. 'The chemical composition of precipitation in adjacent forest and open plots.' *Forestry,* **32,** 14 (1959).
37. BORMANN, F.H. and LIKENS, G.E. 'The watershed ecosystem concept and studies of nutrient cycles.' In *The Ecosystem Concept in Natural Resource Management.* Ed. VAN DYNE, G.M., New York (1969).
38. JORGENSEN, C.A. 'Kvaelstofproblemet paa Maglemose og andre Hojmoser.' *Bot. Tidskr.* **29,** 463 (1927).
39. JENSEN, J. 'Undersogelse over vedborens inhold af plantenaeringsstoffer.' *Tidskr. Pl. Arl.* **65,** 894 (1962).
40. FINNEY, H.R. and FARNHAM, R.S. 'Mineralogy of the inorganic fraction of peat from two raised bogs in Northern Minnesota.' *Proc. 3rd Int. Peat Congress, Quebec,* 102 (1968).
41. BOATMAN, D.J. and ROBERTS, J. 'The amounts of certain nutrients leached from peat by various extractants.' *J. Ecol.* **51,** 187 (1963).
42. GOODMAN, G.T. and PERKINS, D.F. 'The role of mineral nutrients in

Eriophorum communities. IV. Potassium is a limiting factor in an *E. vaginatum* community.' *J. Ecol.* **56,** 685 (1968).

43. BOYD, C.E. 'Production, mineral accumulation and pigment concentrations in *Typha latiofolia* and *Scirpus americanus.' Ecology,* **51,** 285 (1970).
44. ALLEN, S.E. 'Chemical aspects of heather burning.' *J. appl. Ecol.* **1,** 347 (1964)
45. FRANKLAND, J.C. 'Succession of fungi on decaying petioles of *Pteridium aquilinum.' J. Ecol.* **54,** 41 (1966).
46. STEWART, J.M. and ROBERTSON, R.A. 'The chemical status of an exposed peat face.' *Proc. 3rd Int. Peat Congress, Quebec,* 190 (1968).
47. CHAPMAN, S.B. 'Ecology of Coom Rig Moss, Northumberland.' II. Chemistry of peat profiles.' *J. Ecol.* **52,** 315 (1964).
48. BORMANN, F.H. and LIKENS, G.E. 'Nutrient cycling.' *Science,* **155.** 424 (1967).
49. CRISP, D.T. 'Input and output of minerals for an area of Pennine moorland: the importance of precipitation, drainage, peat erosion and animals.' *J. appl. Ecol.* **3,** 327 (1966).
50. LIKENS, G.E., BORMANN, F.H., JOHNSON, N.M. and PIERCE, R.S. 'The calcium, magnesium, potassium and sodium budgets for a small forested ecosystem.' *Ecology,* **48,** 772 (1967).
51. PEARSALL, W.H. *'Mountains and Moorlands.'* London (1950).

Chapter Five

Adaptation in Mire Organisms

All habitats present certain problems to organisms which attempt to occupy them, and such problems, via the agencies of genetic variation and natural selection, eventually lead to the adaptation of the organism in such a way as to render its continued survival more probable. Such adaptation can lead to a high degree of specialisation, be it morphological, anatomical, physiological, biochemical or, in the case of motile organisms, behavioural. Such specifications are mechanisms which enable the organism to overcome some of the problems of its physical and biological environment.

The precise factors which present difficulties to plants and animals vary between different habitats. some being more severe than others. The peatland environment is itself variable, hence some problems are restricted to certain peatland types. In this chapter we shall consider some of these problems together with some of the survival mechanisms which have evolved to overcome them.

The environmental problems associated with peatlands can be considered under three headings:

1. The effects of low oxygen tensions associated with waterlogging
2. In certain mires the level of various mineral ions necessary for growth and survival may be low
3. Temperature fluctuations on mire surfaces, accompanied by changes of humidity can be a problem especially to some animals.

WATERLOGGING

It has long been appreciated that plants living in mires and other aquatic habitats could face problems of oxygen supply necessary for the respiration of submerged tissues. In peaty habitats this problem is magnified by the slow movement of water through the peat.

In 1938 W.H. Pearsall[1] measured potentials within peats with a bright platinum electrode and these he regarded as oxidation—reduction potentials within the peat. The magnitude of these potentials he found to be related to the degree of aeration or waterlogging of the peat and also bore a relationship to the chemical condition of the iron present. If the potential fell below 320—350 mV at pH 5, Fe^{++} ions were found to be present in place of Fe^{+++} ions in peats of higher potential. Sulphate was also reduced to sulphite at this potential and nitrogen was found only as ammonia in peats of low E_h. Pearsall and Mortimer[2] were later able to demonstrate that this changeover in the oxidation—reduction balance of peats occurs at very low oxygen concentrations, ca. 8% saturation. Thus the presence of even very low concentrations of dissolved oxygen ($> 8\%$) is adequate for the maintenance of oxidising conditions within the peat.

Since this early work a considerable amount of data have accumulated concerning the requirements and tolerances of various mire plants. For example, Gore and Urquhart[3] examined the needs of *Molinia caerulea* and *Eriophorum vaginatum* and found that under reducing conditions both the total yield and the root growth of *Eriophorum* were greater than that of *Molinia*. Here *Eriophorum* shows a higher degree of tolerance of low oxygen concentrations which provides it with a competitive advantage over *Molinia* under such conditions. The supply of additional nutrients to the two species resulted in increased yields in both species but they showed no differential response. Hence the adaptation is likely to be one concerned with the low E_h rather than low nutrient levels.

Bannister[4] examined various ericaceous species and found that *Erica tetralix* was entirely unaffected by waterlogging whereas *Erica cinerca* was readily killed by such conditions, having become reduced in its turgour. Jones[5] has since demonstrated that the death of *Erica cinerea* is preceded by a buildup of iron in the plant tissues together with a high rate of transpiration. The two appear to be related since spraying with silicone to reduce transpiration also reduced iron uptake. This enabled plants to survive longer under waterlogged conditions.

The suggestion has been made that reducing conditions may cause an accumulation of toxic compounds around plant roots and Rutter[6] suggests that a fluctuating water table may serve to remove such toxins. This could account for the better performance of *Molinia* under such conditions.

The anatomical and morphological adaptations found in plants associated with waterlogged and anaerobic environments are well known and are summarised by Arber[7]. In particular the development of lacunae and large intercellular spaces is frequent in such plants and Arber demonstrates that such morphological features are especially developed in plants of stagnant waters whereas they may not be present at all in situations where water flow is fast and oxygen supply adequate. For example, the tropical aquatic family *Podostemaceae*

119

require such conditions and die rapidly if placed in stagnant waters; they have no lacunae in their anatomy.

Coult and Vallance[8] examined the gaseous exchanges which take place within the airspace systems of aquatic plants and used the mire plant *Menyanthes trifoliata* as their subject. They suspended 45 cm lengths of *Menyanthes* rhizome within an oxygen free atmosphere while leaving the leafy shoot exposed to air. They observed that oxygen passed the whole length of the rhizome but that at the same time the total oxygen consumption was reduced. Thus such plants do rely upon air spaces for oxygen supply but under anaerobic conditions they are also able to reduce their oxygen demand.

They found that a linear oxygen gradient was set up from the leaves to the petioles to the rhizome and through its length to the roots. Carbon dioxide behaved in precisely the reverse manner, with its highest concentrations in the roots. CO_2 was also found to be the trigger which resulted in reduced oxygen consumption; as CO_2 levels increased in a tissue so oxygen demand was reduced, thus allowing more oxygen to pass through the rhizome to more distal regions. This mechanism may also be interpreted as a process of 'autonarcosis' which reduces respiration rates prior to an 'anaerobic' situation arising where ethyl alcohol might accumulate.

Inevitably some of the oxygen contained within the subaerial parts of such plants must leak into the surrounding medium and it is possible that this local raising of oxygen potentials could be of value to the plant. Armstrong[9] studied this process in a variety of mire plants. He found that the rates of oxygen diffusion from the roots of mire plants were inversely related to the potential under which the plants were found in the field. Some of his results are as follows:

Menyanthes trifoliata	16×10^{-8} g O_2/cm^2 root surface/min.
Eriophorum angustifolium	13×10^{-8} g O_2/cm^2 root surface/min.
Molinia caerulea	1×10^{-8} g O_2/cm^2 root surface/min.

It is possible that this feature is related to Rutter's[6] idea that toxins are produced under reducing conditions; the most tolerant species are those which are able to produce their own locally aerobic root environment by oxygen leakage and hence oxidise toxins. However, as yet there is no evidence for the involvement of such toxins.

Crawford[10] considers that morphological explanations of tolerance of waterlogging are not in themselves adequate to account for the observed facts. He and McManmon[11] have developed a metabolic theory to explain such tolerance. They have shown that lowered oxygen tensions have a direct effect upon glycolytic and respiratory metabolism. In species which are intolerant of flooding, glycolysis becomes accelerated and ethanol is produced under anaerobic conditions. Flood tolerant species, however, have a metabolic switch which diverts glycolysis from producing ethanol to malate. The scheme for a flood intolerant species can be represented as shown in Figure 5.1.

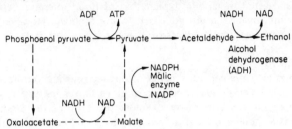

Figure 5.1. Terminal pathways of glycolysis under anaerobic conditions showing the metabolic pathways occuring in flood intolerant species

When flood intolerant species (e.g. *Pisum sativum, Vicia faba, Ammophila arenaria,* etc.) were kept waterlogged for a month it was found that they had much higher alcohol dehydrogenase (ADH) activities than control plants. Under these anaerobic conditions glycolysis was incomplete and the accumulation of acetaldehyde induced ADH activity, leading to a buildup of ethanol. Any malate produced by the alternative pathway shown is decarboxylated to pyruvate by malic enzyme. Thus increased ADH activity leads to a buildup of ethanol which proves toxic to the plant.

In flood tolerant species (e.g. *Mentha aquatica, Caltha paulstris, Glyceria maxima, Iris pseudacorus, Phalaris arundinacea,* etc.) which were kept flooded for the same period there was no accelerated glycolysis or increased ADH activity. In fact, in some species ADH activity was lowered. McManmon and Crawford account for this by an alternative metabolic scheme (see Figure 5.2).

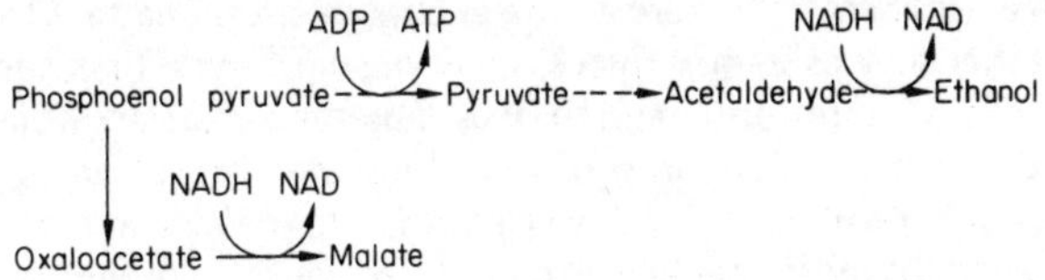

ADP ATP   NADH NAD

Phosphoenol pyruvate ⤵ Pyruvate --→ Acetaldehyde ⤵ Ethanol

          NADH NAD

Oxaloacetate ⤵ Malate

Figure 5.2. The metabolic switch which operates in flood tolerant species diverts glycolysis under anaerobic conditions to malate formation

For these flood tolerant species there is only a partial blockage of the normal respiration. Some ethanol is produced, but there is no induction of enhanced ADH activity. Malic enzyme appears to be inactive, hence there is no decarboxylation of malate and this substance accumulates in the plant tissues. Since malate is nontoxic this proves harmless to the flood tolerant plant.

This suggested metabolic explanation of flood tolerance represents a significant advance in our approach to the problem. However, it has yet to be demonstrated in plants from acidic mire habitats.

NUTRIENTS

In Chapter 4 the general scheme of nutrient cycling in mire systems was discussed and it was observed that certain mire types may be exceedingly deficient in many or most plant nutrients. Under such conditions a number of adaptations may be found in the resident plant species which to some extent counteract this environmental deficiency. Such adaptations may involve

1. Nutrient accumulation and conservation
2. Nitrogen fixation
3. The carnivorous habit.

Nutrient Accumulation and Conservation

A group of plants which is extremely well adapted to growth under conditions of low nutrient supply is the genus *Sphagnum*. The abundance of this group on a world scale and its importance in forming peat deposits, coupled with its ability to survive and grow in water of very low mineral content has resulted in the *Sphagna* attracting much attention from botanists. Early in this century it became evident to botanists that these plants must possess special properties which enable them to accumulate the ions necessary for growth from very dilute solutions and also that they must be able to exert some degree of selectivity in the ions which they absorb. This was first demonstrated experimentally by Skene in 1915[12] and it was known at that time that plant tissues possessed cation exchange properties although nothing was known of the physical or chemical nature of the exchange sites. The fact that such cation exchange was taking place in *Sphagnum* was first shown by Williams and Thompson[13] and it was observed that hydrogen ions exchanged for the cations in solution. Thus the absorption of cations by *Sphagnum* resulted in a lowering of the pH of its immediate environment. Clymo[14] has since considered various other sources of acidity in the vicinity of *Sphagnum*, such as low pH precipitation, the activity of sulphur oxidising bacteria and the secretion of organic acid molecules by living *Sphagnum* plants. However, the first two alternatives are inadequate as explanations of observed pH changes and the organic acid content and composition of bog waters was also too low to be responsible on its own.

Puustjarvi in 1959[15] sought the site of the exchange properties of *Sphagnum* and he proposed that the growing points of the plants continuously formed 'colloidal acids' which were incorporated into the plant structure, and which would produce a potential difference between the internal and external environment resulting in an exchange of hydrogen ions for cations in the surrounding water. Meanwhile, Bell[16] sought a physical explanation of the sites of exchange in terms of submicroscopic channels in the cellulose cell walls which became impregnated with pectic and phenolic compounds, resulting in a structure akin to that of zeolites. This would account for the retention of ion exchange properties after the death of the plant. Bell also demonstrated that trivalent and divalent cations were absorbed much more strongly than monovalent ones.

At this time further work had been proceeding upon the cation exchange properties of all types of plant tissue and in 1961 Knight *et al*[17] confirmed that this exchange capacity was directly correlated with pectic substances. This was achieved by extracting uronic acids from roots of higher plants and showing their relationship with the exchange capacities of these tissues. Clymo in 1963[18] demonstrated this same relationship in *Sphagnum* tissues. Thus the chemical nature of the exchange sites would appear to be unesterified polyuronic acids in the cell walls. These sites, however, could be effective only for cations and Clymo demonstrated that anion exchange in *Sphagnum* was very weak, PO_4''' ions were absorbed only by living *Sphagnum* leaves.

The question then arises whether the exchange capacity of *Sphagnum* is indeed higher than that of other plant tissues and whether it is adequate to account for the acidity of waters from *Sphagnum* dominated mires. Clymo answered both of these questions in the affirmative and in Table 5.1 is a selection of values he measured on a variety of plant tissues. The figures represent the exchange ability of the tissue in m equiv/g dry weight in a solution containing 30 m equiv/litre calcium at a pH of 3.5.

It can be seen that *Sphagnum* does have a higher ability for cation exchange than other plants, especially at this low pH. In general Clymo's results show that most of the bryophyte species he examined have higher exchange properties per unit weight than those of angiosperms and lichens. However the survey is too small for one to be sure that it is representative. Also, as Clymo points out, the possession of

TABLE 5.1

EXCHANGE ABILITY OF PLANT TISSUE m equiv/g dry weight

Calluna vulgaris	(roots)	0·079
Eriophorum angustifolium	(roots)	0·030
Fagus sylvatica	(roots)	0·131
Pellia epiphylla	(whole plant)	0·110
Leucobryum glaucum	(whole plant)	0·123
Aulacomnium palustre	(whole plant)	0·184
Sphagnum spp.	(whole plant)	0·213-0·242

high exchange ability appears to be more closely correlated with taxonomic group than with habitat. Thus *Eriophorum angustifolium* has considerably lower powers of exchange than any other plant Clymo examined.

When examined at a microhabitat level it is found that there is considerable variation in pH between hummock and hollow situations on a mire surface. This is illustrated by the profile in Figure 5.3 which

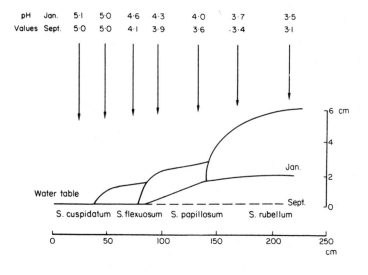

Figure 5.3. pH profile of a pool and hummock and its seasonal variation (after P.J. Beckett, unpublished)

124

is based upon the results of P.J. Beckett at Llyn Mire in Radnorshire. Both in January and in September there is a tendency for pH to fall as one passes from the pool to the hummock, and this fall is more pronounced in September than it is in January. Clymo has demonstrated a close correlation between the exchange ability of *Sphagna* and the height of their optimum habitat above the water table. The mean exchange capacity for three of the sphagna involved in Figure 5.3 are as follows:

S. cuspidatum	0·76 m equiv/g dry weight
S. papillosum	0·94 m equiv/g dry weight
S. rubellum	1·18 m equiv/g dry weight

In all these cases the exchange capacity was measured for calcium at an external concentration of 7.4 m equiv/litre at a pH of 6.0.

Thus hummock forming species such as *S. rubellum* have higher exchange capacities than those in pools. This would lead to a lower pH being generated in the hummock situation. The seasonal changes in pH documented in Figure 5.3 are correlated with seasonal changes in the water table. Higher rates of evaporation in summer could lead to a fall in pH.

The exchange properties of the sphagna are also of importance when we consider larger scale patterns in mire vegetation and temporal changes in mire communities. It has long been recognised that pH decreases as one passes through the vegetational zones surrounding open water. For example, Godwin and Turner[19] showed a fall in pH at Calthorpe Broad, Norfolk, from pH 7 near the open water to pH 5 in the carr regions where *Sphagnum* was established. They considered this spatial zonation to reflect a temporal vegetational succession, thus concluding that the raising of the peat surface relative to the water level, together with changes in the composition of vegetation, resulted in a lowering in pH. They felt that this trend ceased when oak forest established itself. However, it is now disputed whether the oak woodlands of the Broads region can be regarded as the climax of this hydroseral succession[20]. A similar trend of decreasing pH with the progression of a succession may also be reflected in the peat stratigraphy[21] (see Chapter 6). Where such changes are observed, they are often most abrupt at the stage where *Sphagnum* enters the succession.

Thus the cation exchange properties of the sphagna, together with the fast growth rates of certain species can effect considerable changes in their local environment, both by raising the peat surface and by absorbing available cations, especially polyvalent ones. These properties

125

can thus be considered as competitive mechanisms which result in the exclusion of many other species including even trees such as *Betula, Salix, Alnus* and *Pinus* under suitable conditions. Bellamy and Rieley[22] have demonstrated this process in extremely rich rheotrophic fens near Sunbiggin Tarn, Westmorland. In this ecosystem, the deposition of 1804 g/m^2 (8326 kcal/m^2) of peat by *Sphagnum fuscum* resulted in the complete transformation of rheotrophic fen conditions into ombrotrophic bog. Extrapolating from current production rates in *Sphagnum fuscum* they calculated that this process could take as little as seven years. Thus *Sphagnum* must be considered an extremely important and influential genus in mire ecology and development.

However, *Sphagnum* is not the only genus of plants which is able to grow under low nutrient conditions. As yet very few mire plants have been studied in sufficient detail to render possible a full account of nutrient balance and nutrient movements within the plant. One plant which has received considerable attention is *Rubus chamaemorus.* Taylor[23] has reviewed the movements of phosphorus in this blanket bog species through the course of a growing season.

In spring there is an increase in phosphorus uptake prior to bud break and this is coupled with a mobilisation of the phosphorus reserves in the rhizome. Following bud break there is a gradual increase in first stem and then leaf phosphorus which appears to be correlated with increasing peat temperature. The same is true of the roots, where temperatures below 4°C can result in a net loss of phosphorus. Once shoot growth is completed in late summer, phosphorus levels in the shoot begin to fall and this process is accompanied by the production of anthocyanin pigment in the leaves, a feature associated with leaf senescence. It is probable that at this stage the phosphorus from the shoots is mobilised and travels either to the developing fruits or to the rhizome and roots, which may still be growing. Finally, during advanced senescence there is a rapid loss of phosphorus from the shoots accompanied by accumulation in the rhizome and winter buds. Thus within this species which grows under conditions of acute phosphorus shortage, a delicate system of phosphorus conservation has evolved which reduces all unnecessary losses to a minimum.

Goodman and Perkins[24] have observed a similar process in *Eriophorum vaginatum*, where once again there is a mobilisation of reserves in the autumn and a return of nutrients to the perennating organ. This species also has considerable powers of concentration of elements such as phosphorus and potassium. Average values for exchangeable potassium in peat at the site they examined were 0.73 m equiv. K/100 g peat. In the living tissues the concentration was 38 m equiv. K/100 g tissue.

It seems likely that the concentration of essential ions present in low supply together with autumnal mobilisation of reserves and their storage in perennating organs may be a very necessary adaptation for bog plants.

The question of whether phosphorus or potassium is the limiting element for the growth of *Eriophorum* on blanket bog has also been discussed by Goodman and Perkins[25] as well as by Gore[26] and Tamm[27]. The British workers have concluded that potassium is limiting on British blanket bogs, whereas Tamm in Sweden found phosphorus to be limiting. It is possible that this may vary from site to site, depending largely upon the input of these elements via precipitation, which is the only source for blanket bogs. Goodman and Perkins suggest that the invertebrate fauna may play an important role in phosphorus turnover, since if their biomass is high and mortality relatively low they may represent a nonavailable phosphorus reservoir during the growing season and cause stress in the vegetation as a result.

Both phosphorus and potassium are generally at a premium in such situations and any mechanism resulting in their accumulation and retention in living tissues must provide a plant with a high competitive advantage over its neighbours.

Nitrogen Fixation

Another element which is in low supply in anaerobic bog peats is nitrogen in an oxidised, nitrate form which can be absorbed by plant roots. Some bog plant species have evolved alternative methods of enhancing their nitrogen input and one of these is by symbiotic nitrogen fixation.

The bog myrtle *(Myrica gale)* is a species in which symbiotic nitrogen fixation occurs, this process being associated with the root nodules found in this plant[28]. It has been shown by Bond[29] that the rate of nitrogen fixation which occurs in these nodules is comparable with that of legumes. However, the symbiosis in *Myrica* occurs at more acid pH values than is possible in most legumes. Nodules were found to form even at a pH of 3.3, though this is probably the lower limit since many plants failed at this level. If nonnodulated plants were supplied with nitrate—nitrogen at pH 3.3, however, they grew strongly, indicating that it is the process of infection which is limited by this pH rather than the growth of *Myrica*. The rarity of *Myrica* in situations where the pH is below 3.8 may well be associated with problems of infection by the symbiotic organism.

In addition to the difficulties of survival under low pH conditions it may also be expected that the nodules may be subject to oxygen deficiency in an anaerobic environment. However, this is overcome by the production of vertically growing roots which are rich in airspaces[30]. If oxygen supply to these roots is restricted the process of nitrogen fixation is curtailed.

The genus *Alnus* also has nodules in which symbiotic nitrogen fixation occurs and *Alnus glutinosa* is often found under waterlogged conditions in carrs. Bond[31] demonstrated that nitrogen fixation does occur in the field and also that the nitrogen fixed is moved to other parts of the tree. Wheeler[32] has since shown that there is a diurnal fluctuation in the rate of nitrogen fixation in the nodules of both *Alnus* and *Myrica*, being greatest at midday. In *Alnus* this fluctuation is probably due to the increased supply of photosynthate to the nodules during the day time (these photosynthetic products take only ten minutes to reach the nodules from the leaves), possibly reinforced by temperature fluctuations, since nodule fixation is six times faster at $25°C$ than at $15°C$.[33]

As a source of nitrogen input to mire ecosystems, fixation may be locally very important, especially in ombrotrophic mires where *Myrica* may grow. During their first fourteen months of growth *Myrica* plants can fix 460 mg of nitrogen and over 5 000 mg by the end of its third year under experimental (nitrogen free water culture) conditions. In the field even higher rates may occur.[34]

The Carnivorous Habit

An alternative mechanism enabling a plant to supplement its mineral intake is that of trapping and digesting animals. This rather macabre subject has attracted a great deal of attention, especially since Darwin's treatise in 1875[35]. A great deal of the early work, especially on the morphology, anatomy and trapping mechanisms of these plants has been reveiwed by Lloyd[36], whose work remains a very valuable source of reference.

The process of trapping animal life as a nutrient source has evolved in a number of families of flowering plants and is found in a total of almost 500 species. The mechanisms of trapping vary considerably between genera, but there are four main types.

1. The pitfall traps which are passive but are so constructed that an animal which has entered finds it difficult to emerge again (e.g. *Sarracenia* and *Darlingtonia,* plants of ombrotrophic mires of North America).
2. Flypaper traps in which sticky excretions from leaf surface glands lead to insect trapping. These may be active in that the leaves roll inwards following the arrival of a prey organism

(e.g. *Drosera* and *Pinguicula*, the former being found throughout much of the world and the latter confined to the northern hemisphere and South America).

3. Steel traps having sensitive regions which respond to stimulation and result in a sudden and rapid closure entrapping the prey (e.g. *Dionaea* from mires in the southern United States).

4. Suction traps which operate underwater and have sensitive mechanisms which trigger a sudden expansion of the trap, sucking in the prey organism (e.g. *Utricularia*, a genus of worldwide, though mainly tropical, distribution).

No attempt will be made here to describe the complex physiological mechanisms which are involved in the functioning of these traps, nor their intricate morphology. Lloyd[36] provides much information on these subjects. The main advances in knowledge upon these subjects since that time have come through the application of such techniques as electron microscopy and radioautography to the sensitive mechanisms and digestive glands of these plants.

Dionaea muscipula (Venus' fly trap) has probably received more attention than any other carnivorous plant in recent times and has also become a popular novelty house plant. Stuhlman (1951)[37] demonstrated that the stimulation of the sensitive hairs on the leaf of this plant produced an electrical impulse which moved across the leaf lobe to the hinge cells at a rate of 3.0 cm/s. Williams and Mozingo[38] have studied the fine structure of these trigger hairs and associate the generation of this potential with an assymetrical, whorled endoplasmic reticulum in certain sensitive cells at the base of the hairs. This potential may be transmitted from cell to cell via plasmodesmata which are infrequent in lateral and end walls, but abundant in basal walls, thus directing the movement of the signal.

In 1875 Darwin had demonstrated that proteinases and formic acid were produced by the digestive glands of *Dionaea* and also that the growth of some carnivorous plants (e.g. *Utricularia*) was greatly enhanced by the provision of animal prey. Since then Lüttge[39] has used radioautographic techniques to trace the absorption of labelled compounds and their subsequent distribution within the plant. ^{14}C glutamic acid, $^{35}SO_4''$ and $^{45}Ca^{++}$ were used to trace nutrient movements and Lüttge followed the distribution of these substances throughout the plant within 7—10 days of trapping the prey. 36 hours after closure measurable quantities of proteolytic enzymes are secreted by the digestive glands[40] and this process is accompanied by fine structural changes in these glands.[41]

The use of scanning electron microscopy, in which surfaces can be studied at high magnifications rather than sections, has proved very valuable in the examination of leaf surface topography and gland structure. It has been applied to *Dionaea*[42] and also to *Pinguicula*[43] where Heslop-Harrison has produced impressive photographs of the arrangement of stalked and sessile glands. In this plant the stalked glands are mucilage secreting and adhere to the prey while the sessile glands secrete enzymes including phosphatases, proteases, ribonuclease, etc., involved in digestion.

Although the nutrient input from the carnivorous habit is of considerable importance for the survival and growth of the individual plant, there are as yet no data from which one might ascertain the importance of this process to the mire ecosystem as a whole.

TEMPERATURE

The surfaces of mires absorb and radiate long wavelength radiation extremely efficiently and this can result in considerable seasonal and diurnal fluctuations in surface temperatures. In addition, the wetness of conditions just below the surface can lead to a very steep gradient of temperature as one descends into the peat.

In addition to the steep temperature profile within the upper few centimetres of peat, there is also a rapid change in relative humidity operating in the opposite direction. Norgaard (1951)[44] has published temperature and humidity figures for a Danish *Sphagnum* bog in July which demonstrate this inverse relationship (see Table 5.2).

TABLE 5.2
TEMPERATURE AND HUMIDITY VALUES FOR A DANISH
SPHAGNUM BOG (Norgaard, 1951[44])

	Diurnal temperature fluctuation	Relative humidity
100 cm above mire surface	26°C	
At mire surface	33°C	< 40%
100 cm below surface	5°C	100%

Most invertebrate animals are extremely sensitive to temperature and relative humidity and it might well be expected that such steep profiles as those exhibited by *Sphagnum* mires should have considerable influence upon the dispersal and behaviour of such animals. Norgaard has demonstrated this most ably in two species of lycosid spiders, *Lycosa pullata* and *Pirata piraticus* from Danish mires.

Lycosa pullata is an ubiquitous spider in western Europe, but in the east becomes restricted to wet situations. It is frequent on mires, reaching densities of 12 per square metre at Norgaard's site. It inhabits the surface layers of the mire where it runs over the capitula of the *Sphagnum* plants.

Pirata piraticus in Continental Europe is found only in very moist conditions, often being associated with free water surfaces. In the Danish *Sphagnum* bogs it lives beneath the capitula of the moss in the stalk layer (Figure 5.4).

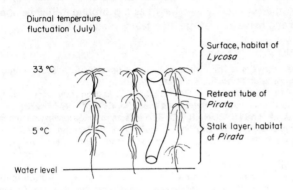

Figure 5.4.   Ecology of two spiders on Danish Sphagnum bogs (after Norgaard[44])

After copulation, the female *Pirata* builds a retreat tube 6—8 cm long and open at both ends which leads from the stalk layer up to the mire surface. The egg cocoon is taken up to the surface and exposed to the sun while the female sits in the tube facing downwards, ready to retreat in the event of any disturbance. In this position, one assumes, the cocoon can receive the high temperatures necessary for egg development and yet the adult spider can avoid overheating.

In an experiment to examine the behavioural mechanism involved in this process, Norgaard placed the two species in a temperature preferendum apparatus where the spiders were offered a choice between two chambers, one at 18—24°C and the other at 26—32°C. All the *Lycosa* individuals irrespective of sex chose the chamber at the higher temperature. The *Pirata* males and females without egg cocoons chose the cool chamber, but females with egg cocoons preferred the 26—32°C chamber. Thus a different behavioural mechanism comes into play in *Pirata* females with eggs which causes them to seek the higher temperatures found at the *Sphagnum* surface in day time.

In addition to this behavioural mechanism in *Pirata*, Norgaard found

131

an adaption in *Lycosa* allowing it to tolerate the greater extremes of temperature fluctuation at the mire surface. *Lycosa* individuals could tolerate temperatures as low as 12.7°C before becoming inactive, whereas this happened to *Pirata* at 17.0°C. At the other end of the scale, *Lycosa* did not suffer from heat stupor until 43.0°C whereas *Pirata* was affected at 35.3°C.

Thus the thermal stratification of mires, together with their diurnal and seasonal temperature fluctuations produces a complex of micro-habitats in the surface layers which has a profound influence upon the dispersion and behaviour of the invertebrate fauna.

REFERENCES

1. PEARSALL, W.H. 'The soil complex in relation to plant communities. III. Moorlands and bogs.' *J. Ecol.* **26**, 298 (1938).
2. PEARSALL, W.H. and MORTIMER, C.H. 'Oxidation-reduction potentials in waterlogged soils, natural waters and muds.' *J. Ecol.* **27**, 483 (1939).
3. GORE, A.J.P. and URQUHART, C. 'The effects of waterlogging on the growth of *Molinia caerulea* and *Eriophorum vaginatum.*' *J. Ecol.* **54**, 617 (1966).
4. BANNISTER, P. 'The water relations of certain heath plants with reference to their ecological amplitude. III. Experimental studies: general conclusions.' *J. Ecol.* **52**, 499 (1964).
5. JONES, H.E. 'Comparative studies of plant growth and distribution in relation to waterlogging. II. An experimental study of the relationship between transpiration and the uptake of iron in *Erica cinera* L. and *E. tetralix* L. *J. Ecol.* **59**, 167 (1971).
6. RUTTER, A.J. 'Composition of wet heath vegetation in relation to the water table.' *J. Ecol.* **43**, 507 (1955).
7. ARBER, A. *'Water Plants.'* Cambridge (1920).
8. COULT, D.A. and VALLANCE, K.B. 'Observations on the gaseous exchanges which take place between *Menyanthes trifoliata* L. and its environment. II.' *J. exp. Bot.* **9**, 384 (1958).
9. ARMSTRONG, W. 'Oxygen diffusion from the roots of some British bog plants.' *Nature, Lond.* **204**, 801 (1964).
10. CRAWFORD, R.M.M. 'The physiological basis of flooding tolerance.' *Ber. dt. bot. Ges.* **82**, 111 (1969).
11. McMANMON, M. and CRAWFORD, R.M.M. 'A metabolic theory of flooding tolerance: the significance of enzyme distribution and behaviour.' *New Phytol.* **70**,299 (1971).
12. SKENE, M. 'The acidity of *Sphagnum* and its relation to chalk and mineral salts.' *Ann. Bot.* **29**, 65 (1915).
13. WILLIAMS, K.T. and THOMPSON, T.G. 'Experiments on the effect of *Sphagnum* on the pH of salt solutions.' *Int. Rev. Hydrobiol.* **33**, 271 (1936).
14. CLYMO, R.S. 'The origin of acidity in *Sphagnum* bogs.' *Bryologist,* **67**, 427 (1964).
15. PUUSTJÄRVI, V. 'On the cation uptake mechanism of *Sphagnum* mosses.' *Maatoloustieteelinen Aikakauskirja,* **31**, 103 (1959).
16. BELL, P.R. 'The ability of *Sphagnum* to absorb cations preferentially from dilute solutions resembling natural waters.' *J. Ecol.* **47**, 351 (1959).
17. KNIGHT, A.J., CROOKE, W.M. and INKSON, R.H.E. 'Cation exchange

capacities of tissues of higher and lower plants and their related uronic acid contents.' *Nature, Lond.* **192,** 142 (1961).

18. CLYMO, R.S. 'Ion exchange in *Sphagnum* and its relation to bog ecology.' *Ann. Bot.* N.S, **27,** 309 (1963).

19. GODWIN, H. and TURNER, J.S. 'Soil acidity in relation to vegetational succession in Calthorpe Broad, Norfolk.' *J. Ecol.* **21,** 235 (1933).

20. LAMBERT' J.M. 'The vegetation of Broadland.' In *The Broads.* E.A. Ellis, London (1965).

21. CHAPMAN, S.B. 'The ecology of Coom Rigg Moss, Northumberland. II. The chemistry of peat profiles and the development of the bog system.' *J. Ecol.* **52,** 315 (1964).

22. BELLAMY, D.J. and RIELEY, J. 'Some ecological statistics of a miniature bog.' *Oikos,* **18,** 33 (1967).

23. TAYLOR, K. 'Biological flora of the British Isles. *Rubus chamaemorus L.' J. Ecol.* **59,** 293 (1971).

24. GOODMAN, G.T. and PERKINS, D.F. 'Mineral uptake and retention in cotton grass *(Eriophorum vaginatum L.).' Nature, Lond.* **184,** 467 (1959).

25. GOODMAN, G.T. and PERKINS, D.F. 'The role of mineral nutrients in *Eriophorum* communities. IV. Potassium supply as a limiting factor in an *E. vaginatum* community.' *J. Ecol.* **56,** 685 (1968).

26. GORE, A.J.P. 'Factors limiting plant growth on high-level blanket peat. II. Nitrogen and phosphate in the first year of growth.' *J. Ecol.* **49,** 605 (1961).

27. TAMM, C.O. 'Some observations on the nutrient turnover in a bog community dominated by *Eriophorum vaginatum* L.' *Oikos,* **5,** 189 (1954).

28. BOND, G. 'Root nodules of bog myrtle or sweet gale *(Myrica gale* L.)' *Nature, Lond.* **163,** 730 (1948).

29. BOND, G. 'The fixation of nitrogen associated with the root nodules of *Myrica gale* L. with special reference to its pH relation and ecological significance.' *Ann. Bot.* N.S. **15,** 447 (1951).

30. BOND, G. 'Some features of root growth in nodulated plants of *Myrica gale* L.' *Ann. Bot.* N.S. **16,** 467 (1952).

31. BOND, G. 'Evidence for fixation of nitrogen by root nodules of alder under field conditions.' *New Phytol.* **55,** 147 (1956).

32. WHEELER, C.T. 'The diurnal fluctuation in nitrogen fixation in the nodules of *Alnus glutinosa* and *Myrica gale.' New Phytol.* **68,** 675 (1969).

33. WHEELER' C.T. 'The causation of diurnal changes in nitrogen fixation in the nodules of *Alnus glutinosa.' New Phytol.* **70,** 487 (1971).

34. BOND, G. and GARDNER, I.C. 'Nitrogen fixation in non-legume root nodulated plants.' *Nature, Lond.* **179,** 680 (1957).

35. DARWIN, C. *Insectivorous Plants.* New York (1875).

36. LLOYD, F.E. *The Carnivorous Plants.* Waltham, Mass. (1942).

37. STUHLMAN, O. 'An analysis of the bioelectric action potential produced in the lobes of the Venus' flytrap by mechanical stimulation.' *Phys. Rev.* **83,** 877 (1951).

38. WILLIAMS, M.E. and MOZINGO, H.N. 'The fine structure of the trigger hair in Venus' flytrap.' *Amer. J. Bot.* **58,** 532 (1971).

39. LÜTTGE, U. 'Die Bedentung des chemischen Reizes bei der Resorption von ^{14}C-glutaminsaure, $^{35}SO_4$++ und ^{45}Ca++ durch *Dionaea muscipula.' Naturwissenschaften.* **50,** 22 (1963).

40. SIMMONS' E., MATTIMOE, K., SCHWAB, D.W. and SCALA, J. 'Hydrolytic enzyme elaborations of Venus' flytrap.' *Amer. J. Bot.* **55,** 714 (1968).

41. SCHWAB, D.W., SIMMONS, E. and SCALA, J. 'Fine structure changes during function of the digestive gland of Venus' flytrap.' *Amer. J. Bot.* **56**, 88 (1969).
42. MOZINGO, H.N., KLEIN, P., ZEEVI, Y. and LEWIS, E.R. 'Venus' flytrap observations by scanning electron microscopy.' *Amer. J. Bot.* **47**, 593 (1970).
43. HESLOP-HARRISON, Y. 'Scanning electron microscopy of fresh leaves of *Pinguicula.' Science,* **167**, 172 (1970).
44. NOORGAARD, E. 'On the ecology of two Lycosid spiders *(Pirata piraticus* and *Lycosa pullata)* from a Danish *Sphagnum* bog.' *Oikos,* **3**, 1 (1951).

Chapter Six

Peat Stratigraphy - a Record of Succession

So far we have considered peat simply as a resource of energy and nutrients locked up in a form unavailable to the biota of the ecosystem. However, its scientific interest does not merely lie in this property. Peat has a structure of its own and it is to the study of this structure that we now turn.

We saw in Chapter 4 how plant and animal litter falling onto the surface of a mire might undergo decomposition or, if the rate of litter accretion was great and the microbial activity relatively low, it might pass into the sulphide zone where decomposition rates were extremely low. Once in this zone, therefore, plant and animal remains stand a reasonably good chance of prolonged survival; the only additional change which they may suffer will be compression under the weight of deposits accumulating above. The critical factor, therefore, in the preservation of such material is the speed of entry into the sulphide zone.

Two types of materials are likely to be favoured selectively in preservation, namely those plant organs which penetrate the peat and which are therefore closer to the sulphide zone on death, i.e. roots and rhizomes, and those portions of plants and animals which are constructed of materials which are relatively resistant to microbial attack, e.g. lignin, suberin, chitin. These latter structures, though deposited on the mire surface, are more likely to survive their period of residence in the upper peat layers.

Peat therefore consists of the following components:

1. Organic matter in an organised state of preservation and therefore identifiable
2. Organic matter which has undergone considerable breakdown but in which cell structure is still visible; normally not recognisable to any degree
3. Organic matter which has been degraded below the cellular level, composing what might be termed 'humus' and often forming a peat matrix
4. Inorganic matter, either derived from dust or inwash, or from the cells of some plants, e.g. silica phytoliths from grasses or diatom frustules.

The proportion of each of these components will vary from one peat sample to another within the profile, depending upon the nature of the peat forming material, the rate of decomposition and the rate of breakdown in the aerobic layers. Some workers have found it useful to develop a scale of humification in peat which provides an estimate of this characteristic.

Many peats, then, contain recognisable fragments of the vegetation which formed them. Add to this the fact that most peats *in situ* remain stratified in the sequence in which they are laid down and one has the potential for tracing the course of vegetational succession. Peat forming ecosystems are exceptional in possessing within themselves a record of their historical development in the form of peat. This feature has rendered peatlands of particular interest to those who have an interest in the history and development of modern plant and animal communities.

Traditionally, if somewhat arbitrarily, the subfossil component of peats has been divided into macrofossils and microfossils on the basis of their size. We shall concentrate upon the former for the present, since these are the fossils derived mainly from local vegetation and which are therefore of greatest value in the reconstruction of mire history. Microfossils are frequently derived from vegetation considerable distances away and therefore the interpretation of such assemblages poses rather different problems. We shall consider these and the conclusions possible from the study of microfossils in a later chapter.

For the moment let us consider the nature of the macrofossil component of peat and methods of studying it. We shall then be in a position to look at the implications of these studies in the investigation of peat stratigraphy and mire development.

MACROFOSSIL TYPES

Macrofossils have always been regarded as those subfossil remains which can be recognised without the aid of high powered microscopy. However, in point of fact this is often necessary even when such large objects as leaves and seeds are to be identified to the level of species. Recent detailed work on macrofossils has even employed the use of scanning electron microscopy, e.g. for the examination of sculpturing on the testa of seeds[2]. A full, illustrated analysis of Quaternary plant subfossil records is given by Godwin (1956)[3].

For the convenience of discussion we can divide macrofossils into four groups:
1. Nonwoody, plant vegetative organs
2. Wood

3. Plant reproductive structures

4. Animal fossils.

The nonwoody plant vegetative organs include both above and below ground parts. The below ground parts, roots and rhizomes, are extremely common constituents of peat deposits. Their overrepresentation is inevitable in view of the advantage they possess in terms of the time taken to enter the sulphide zone. However, their usefulness for tracing vegetational history is limited for two main reasons. In the first place, the fact that they penetrate into deeper layers of peat means that their final position in the peat stratigraphy will be below the true position for the species. Thus the presence of root material of a species cannot be interpreted as indicating that the species grew upon the mire surface contemporaneous with that level.

The second disadvantage of roots is the difficulty experienced in identification. Some rhizomes and stem bases can be identified, e.g. *Cladium mariscus, Phragmites communis, Carex limosa* and *Scheuchzeria palustris,* but roots, expecially in the Cyperaceae cannot be separated satisfactorily.

Of the above ground parts, leaves are both recognisable, often to species level, and are deposited on the contemporary mire surface. When intact, identification is relatively simple on the basis of their shape, margin and venation, e.g. *Salix herbacea* (see Figure 6.1). Epidermal features, particularly stomata, are valuable for the identification of leaves of Gramineae and Cyperaceae.

The woody portions of plants often survive well in peat and their anatomical structure may render them identifiable. Various descriptions and keys are available for wood identification from a series of sections, e.g. Godwin[3] and Jane[4], using such features as the arrangement of vessels, rays and their structure. These are usually adequately preserved in peat. In the case of twigs, bark structure can also be useful in identification.

Bryophyte remains are often exceedingly abundant in peat deposits, particularly *Sphagnum* species. Many of these can be specifically identified from their leaf size and shape or from cellular characters. Some other mosses, e.g. *Polytrichum* spp. and *Drepanocladus* spp. may also form the bulk of certain peat deposits and isolated remains of many species may occur. Liverworts, on the other hand, are uncommon in peats, possibly due to their poor survival.

Lichens also are grossly underrepresented in peats. Richardson and Green[5] have recorded the crustaceous lichen *Pyrenula nitida* on bark from a peat deposit at Wyburnbury Moss, Cheshire, dating from approximately 500 B.C. Other Pleistocene subfossil lichens are discussed by Sernander[6] and Klenent[7], but generally records are scarce. Richardson

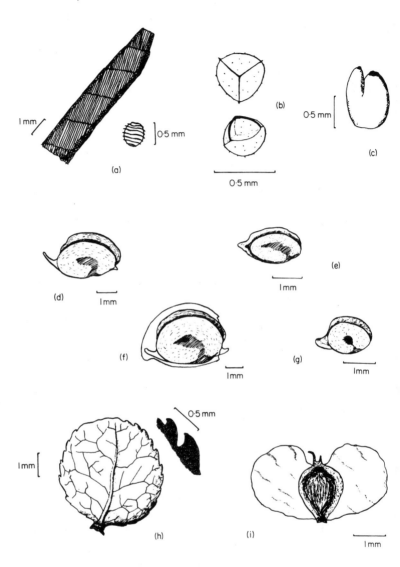

Figure 6.1. Examples of macrofossils found in peat deposits and lake sediments
(a) *Chara sp.* (alga) filament and oospore (b) *Selaginella selaginoides*
megaspore (c) *Subularia aquatica* seed (d) *Potamogeton obtusifolius*
fruit (e) *P. pusillus* fruit (f) *P. natans* fruit (g) *P.polygonifolius* fruit
(h) *Salix herbacea* leaf (i) *Betula pubescens* fruit

and Green consider that crustose species adhering closely to bark are more likely to be preserved than fruticose ones. The records appear to confirm this.

Pteriodophytes are occasionally represented in peat deposits, particularly by sporangia, though also occasionally by fronds and rhizomes.

Angiosperm reproductive structures can be very valuable in that they are often recognisable to the level of species. In particular fruits and seeds have been of considerable use in reconstructing the history of mires, and vegetational history in general. The precision with which such structures can be recognised and the features involved in their identification are reviewed by C.A. Dickson[2]. On the whole such seeds are derived from local mire vegetation, hence families such as Cyperaceae, Ericaceae, Caryophyllaceae and Ranunculaceae figure prominently. However, seeds and fruits from further afield may enter the mire system by downwash, or by aerial transport, e.g. the winged fruits of *Betula* (see Figure 6.2). These seeds may be extracted from a peat sample by flotation on 10% nitric acid, removal of the froth containing seeds and sieving to separate the different sizes[8].

The most frequent animal remains to be found in peats are the chitinous exoskeletons of arthropods, particularly mites and beetles. The former can also be recovered from peat by flotation[9].

Although the bulk of the material of which peat is composed consists of macroscopic plant and animal remains, or their derivatives, there is an additional component, viz. the microfossils, which are of considerable interest to palaeoecologists. If a peat sample is digested in 10% potassium hydroxide, much of the 'humic' material, i.e. the organic soil colloid, is removed, When the larger fragments remaining are sieved off one is left with a fine material consisting of small, particulate plant and animal debris, pollen grains and fungal spores, in varying proportions. The concentration of pollen grains by this technique was pioneered by von Post in the early part of this century and it has been applied by many workers in many modified forms to deposits in all parts of the world. In this way much has been learned about the history of vegetation.

Pollen has a number of advantages and disadvantages for this type of study. In the first place the sculpturing of the pollen grain surface is distinctive and permits identification often to generic and occasionally to specific level. As microscopic techniques improve and as various difficult groups are subjected to closer scrutiny, so the precision involved in pollen identification becomes greater [10, 11, 12]. Often, however, fruits and seeds can be identified with greater certainty. Secondly pollen peat may be derived from considerable distances as a result of aerial transport.

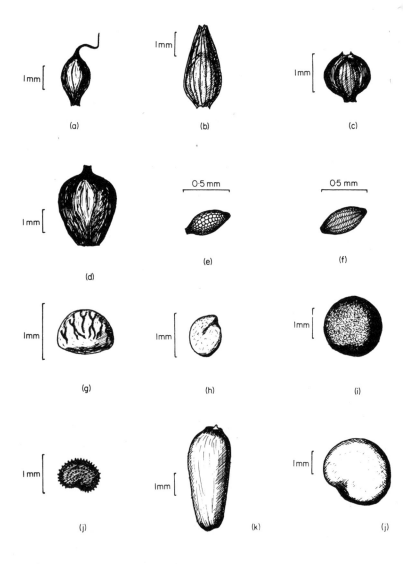

Figure 6.2   *Further examples of plant macrofossils*
(a) Carex rostrata nut (b) C. acutiformis nut and utricle (c) C. flacca
nut and utricle (d) Scirpus lacustris fruit (e) Juncus cf. articulatus
seed (g) Ranunculus (subgenus Batrachium) achene (h) R. sceleratus
achene (i) Galium palustre fruit (j) Lychnis flos-cuculi seed
(k) Cirsium palustre fruit (l) Menyanthes trifoliata seed

Its presence is therefore of less value than macroscopic remains to those who are concerned with reconstructing mire successions. It is more valuable, however, for the study of regional vegetational changes. Pollen does have the advantage of being abundant so that one is better able to count and express the proportions of different types present. These problems and the application of the study of pollen grains will be discussed in detail in the next chapter.

Fungal spores are often abundant in peat, but have received very little attention. Again one has the problem of long distance transport of these microfossils. It has been demonstrated by Hurst and Stedman[13] that such transport can occur over several thousands of miles under appropriate meteorological conditions. Thus, once again, the application of fungal spore studies to local vegetational change is limited.

It can be seen that peat is an intricate mixture of plant and animal remains of various sizes and forms. The nature of the peat depends largely upon the plant community giving rise to the deposit. In some peat forming deposits, e.g. *Phragmites* reed swamp, the vegetation is extremely uniform and hence a homogenous peat is formed. However, other peat types are extremely heterogenous as a result of a high intensity of pattern in the peat forming vegetation. Stewart and Durno[14] have studied such variations in peat structure in a *Calluna* dominated blanket peat in east Scotland. They mapped the small scale variations in three dimensions and found a complexity of peat types which reflected the diversity of surface vegetation and changing water regime of the site.

Despite such local changes in peat structure it has proved possible to classify peats on the basis of the vegetation which formed them and which thus contributes the largest proportion of the macroscopic plant materials. These peat types fall into three broad classes depending upon the water regime in which they are formed.

1. *Limnic peats* are formed below water level
2. *Telmatic peats* accumulate in the zone which is periodically immersed and emersed and
3. *Terrestric peats* are produced above the general water level.

The limnic peats may consist of redeposited material, that is terrestric or telmatic peats which have been eroded and have settled out under lake conditions. Materials deposited in a position where they did not originally grow are termed allochthonous. Other limnic peats are autochthonous, being deposited in the place where they were formed. The type of peat forming vegetation and the type of peat produced vary according to whether the lake waters are eutrophic or oligotrophic. The former type of lake will produce a rich assemblage of floating macrophytic vegetation, whereas base-poor situations may be dominated by a single species, e.g. a floating mat of *Carex rostrata* which produces a uniform limnic peat of rhizome and leaf detritus together with the characteristic nuts of the species. Sometimes *Sphagnum cuspidatum* becomes important in such situations and the deposit may consist of *Sphagnum* leaves in a matrix of gelatinous mud which is very rich in pollen. These conditions are termed dystrophic and the mud is sometimes referred to as dy[10]. Limnic peats are symbolised in diagrams by diagonal cross-hatching.

Telmatic peats are most frequent in rheotrophic situations where a variety of plant species may be important in the process of peat formation. *Phragmites* is often an important component, or, under very calcareous conditions, *Cladium.* However, other plants such as *Carex* spp, *Equisetum, Juncus* or mosses of the 'hypnoid' types may be locally dominant and give rise to a distinctive peat type. Rheotrophic, telmatic peats have been traditionally represented in diagrams by vertical parallel lines, some authors distinguishing the dominant plant type by the relative spacing of lines, e.g. *Phragmites* widely spaced and *Carex* closely spaced. *Cladium* peat symbols often include the use of diamond symbols[3,10].

Telmatic peat may also form under ombrotrophic conditions. Semi-aquatic Sphagna such as *S. cuspidatum* and *S. subsecundum* may be involved, or some of the acidophyllic Cyperaceae, e.g. *Carex rostrata, C. lasiocarpa* and *Scheuchzeria palustris.* The latter type forms distinctive layers in many bogs in western Britain[15] and is often given a symbol of its own[3].

Rheotrophic terrestric peats are often formed by carr communities, that is waterlogged woodland, frequently of alder or birch. These peats are represented by 'V' symbols in diagrams.

Ombrotrophic terrestric peats form the bulk of many deposits in northern Europe and the commonest peat forming vegetation contains considerable quantities of *Sphagnum* species. Frequently there are many species of sphagna represented in such deposits, but occasionally a single species dominates, e.g. *Sphagnum imbricatum* or *S. fuscum.* Other plants are usually present in such peats in lesser quantities such as *Calluna* and other Ericaceous genera. In general this component becomes more prominent as the degree of humification increases; in other words as the conditions under which the peat was formed become drier. *Sphagnum* peats, including *Sphagnum/Calluna* peats are usually symbolised by a series of wavy lines.

Eriophorum species may also be present in such peats, and sometimes *E. vaginatum* totally dominates a peat type. The presence of these plants is represented by zigzag lines.

142

A final terrestric peat type is that made up largely of grass remains, particularly *Molinia caerulea.* Horizontal, parallel lines are used to represent this peat type, which is often highly humified and oxidised.

PEAT STRATIGRAPHY

Since peat is laid down in a stratified manner one can trace the development of a mire by studying the succession of peat types in its profile. Such profiles are not often exposed, except perhaps as a result of peat digging, but they can still be studied using an auger which will extract cores of peat from the required depth[16]. Generally these work on the principle of rotating a moveable chamber once the sampling head is at the required depth and cutting a core from the peat at that level with a minimum of disturbance. Most types of sampler in current use extract a core 50 cm in length which can be removed to the laboratory for examination.

A number of such borings are necessary before a development profile can be constructed, the precise number being determined by the degree of change in stratigraphy between one boring and the next. If there is considerable difference between adjacent borings then intermediate ones need to be examined in order to clarify transitional zones.

Examination of the macroscopic, subfossil remains in such cores allows the peat to be classified into a major type or a mixture of types. For most purposes it is possible to carry out such a determination in the field with the aid of a hand lens, but obviously the degree of precision is considerably improved if the cores can be removed to the laboratory intact.

Once the peat types have been identified and the boundaries between one type and its successor have been established it is possible to draw up a profile, such as the ones shown in Figures 6.3 and 6.4. It is usual to exaggerate the vertical axis as shown in this diagram in order to demonstrate more effectively the topographic features of the mire. Often diagrams are drawn in the form of complete profiles, as in Figure 6.5, but strictly this involves going beyond the scope of the available data. Borings have been taken at a series of points along the profile and the peat stratigraphy has been studied in detail at these points. On some diagrams the sampling points are indicated, but even if they are not one can usually detect them by the deflections in the boundary lines between peat types. However, we have no direct knowledge of the behaviour of the peat types in between these samples. Where there is little difference between adjacent borings one may be reasonably justified in assuming regularity in the intervening area, but frequently this assumption is not at all justifiable. Increasing the number of sampling points helps in the

143

alleviation of this problem, and often smooths out such differences, but one is still not strictly justified in joining the boundary levels between adjacent samples. An alternative way of expressing the data is to represent each sampling point separately, perhaps adding tentative correlation lines to facilitate the task of understanding the trends of vegetational succession demonstrated in the profile. Figures 6.3 and 6.4 are diagrams of this type.

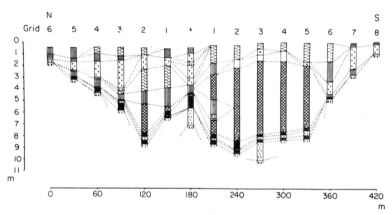

Figure 6.3. Stratigraphical section of Llyn Mire, Radnorshire, in north-south section. Sediment symbols are shown in Figure 6.5.

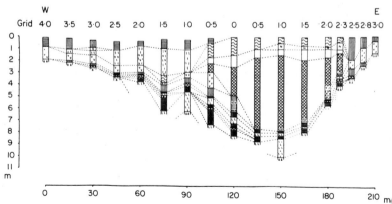

Figure 6.4. Stratigraphical profile of Llyn Mire taken at right angles to the section shown in Figure 6.3. The profiles intersect at the point S3 and E10.

144

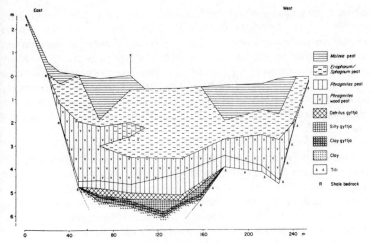

Figure 6.5. *Stratigraphical section of the Elan Valley mire*

Figure 6.5 shows the stratigraphic profile of a mire at Elan Valley in upland mid-Wales[17], and it demonstrates a number of features which are commonly met with in such situations. At an altitude of 384 m, this mire occupies a steep sided depression in an area of Silurian shale, a bedrock poor in mineral nutrients. The base of the depression is irregular due to deposits of glacial till which are thickest on the western side. The eastern side is thus deeper and its basal sediments are clays, silts and muds which accumulate under lacustrine conditions at the close of the last (Devensian) glacial epoch[18]. This shallow lake became infilled and gave way to a *Phragmites* dominated fen, which became invaded by birch, *Betula pubescens* and later by pine. The carr peat gradually gives way to an *Eriophorum* dominated peat with some *Sphagnum* together with *Calluna.* In the periferal regions of the mire the uppermost peats have been formed by *Molinia.*

We can interpret the early stages of this mire stratigraphy as a hydroseral succession resulting from the gradual silting of a glacial lake. This lake was fairly calcareous, containing the remains of such calcium demanding genera as the alga *Chara,* but the fen which invaded the shallow lake was rather poor in calcicole species and some of the remains, e.g. *Sphagnum squarrosum* show that nutrient input to the mire was rather less than that experienced by the lake. This is probably due to the deterioration of local soils as precipitation and leaching gradually removed the soluble ions from it and flushed them into the mire. Such

145

nutrients may have been relatively abundant after the severe weathering experienced at the close of the glaciation, but would diminish as weathering processes slowed in the improving climate. So leaching exceeded weathering and the nutrient supply to the mire became smaller. Eventually the nutrient input became inadequate to maintain carr vegetation and cotton sedge mire developed. It is natural that this process would have been initiated in the central regions of the mire where the influence of drainage waters from the surrounding area would have been least.

It can be seen that the carr survived for much longer around the edges of the mire, being maintained by the slight flushing effect of drainage. It appears to have spread out into the mire once again at one stage in the east. It may be that increased precipitation locally flushed the eastern margin. Subsequently carr vegetation was lost over the whole mire, being replaced around the edges by *Molinia* swamp. This vegetation type can be maintained in a poorer nutrient regime than can carr, hence it must be regarded as a further step towards acid, nutrient-poor conditions. The recent spread of *Molinia* onto the central parts of the mire is likely to be due to a number of factors, e.g.

1. peat erosion and local drying of the mire surface
2. the increased grazing of sheep in historical times, hence eutrophication and
3. increased burning by man.

A depth of two metres corresponds to the level at which signs of human activity are first to be found in the microfossil component of the peat (see Chapter 7).

Thus the stratigraphic profile of a mire can be of immense value in tracing its development and therefore in the understanding of the present vegetation of the mire. It helps us to determine what ecological factors are of greatest influence at the present day and also may give a clue as to the developmental trends through which the mire is currently passing. Such a knowledge is vital for the conservation and management of a mire.

As we saw in Chapter 3, there is considerable variety in the form and surface vegetation of mires and the same applies to their stratigraphy. The type we have just described is frequent in steep sided depressions in areas of nutrient-poor soils. Figure 6.6. shows a series of profiles through the mire at Malham, Yorks[19] which has developed on an irregular deposit of till overlying shale. It is not as steep sided as the Elan Valley mire but is at a similar altitude. It also differs in that much of the water draining into the mire is derived from limestone rocks and hence is highly calcareous. These two factors have influenced the course of succession at this site.

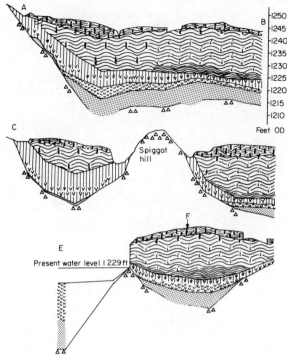

In the early stages of development at the close of the Devensian glaciation an extensive lake occupied the site and within this highly calcareous lake marl sediments were deposited. As at Elan valley, the shallower areas of this lake became invaded by fen, in this case largely by sedges. This fen gave way to a birch carr with some hazel *(Corylus avellana)*. The invasion of *Sphagnum* which followed was restricted to those areas which were furthest from the influence of calcareous drainage water and depended largely upon direct precipitation for their water supply. These regions became more ombrotrophic and gave way to bog vegetation, but this must be regarded as a result of their isolation from drainage water rather than of soil deterioration as was the case in mid-Wales. The complex basal topography at Malham resulted in the formation of a number of small bogs in the centre of each hollow area, each surrounded by a rich fen carr. As *Sphagnum* peat accumulated so many of these small bogs coalesced to form larger bogs, raised above their surroundings by active peat growth and becoming increasingly independent of the underlying topography. Eventually one large domed mire was formed, interrupted only by the till outcrop of Spiggot Hill and

147

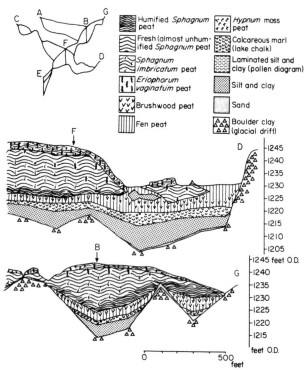

Figure 6.6. Stratigraphy of Tarn Moss, Malham. The vertical scales are in feet above Ordnance Datum

still possessing an extensive fen carr along its one side (area D) where the calcareous drainage water from the limestone circumscribes the bog.

The production of domed mires of this type required a larger area with less steep sides than was provided by the Elan Valley site. There the central growth of peat was matched by peripheral growth. Perhaps the supply of strongly calcareous waters around the edge of the mire at Malham would also serve to reduce the peripheral accumulation of peat. The bulk of the central peat is composed of *Sphagnum imbricatum,* a species which is now very local in the British Isles, but which is a frequent component of such bog peats in many parts of the country. This species forms large dense hummocks which often remain very poorly humified in the peat which make it a very conspicuous component. Some possible explanation for its current rarity in the light of its former abundance have been considered by Green[20].

148

The bog at Malham is basically similar in its development to that at the Elan Valley: the differences which occur being mainly due to factors of nutrient supply and the shape of the hollow in which it was formed. A rather different type of development is shown at a small mire called Llyn in Radnorshire (see Figures 6.3 and 6.4)[21]. This also occupies a hollow in glacial till which is formed in the site of a late glacial lake. Its present vegetation consists of a *Sphagnum* bog in the southeast region with scattered pines, a birch carr around its edge and disturbed areas with pine, *Eriophorum* and *Molinia* in the western and northern areas. The stratigraphy at this site is rather complex. The southeastern side is deeper than other parts of the mire and is to some extent isolated by ridges of till. Drainage of the mire is by a stream which runs out at the north end. A lake occupied the entire basin at the end of the glaciation and persisted for some while subsequently. It then became invaded by reedswamp around its edges and along the ridges of till, eventually completely closing the northern and western sides of the mire and extending out into the southeast basin. However a change then occurred in this familiar sequence of hydroseral succession. The fen and carr areas around the perimeter of the southeast lake became flooded and in the stratigraphy are replaced by further lake deposits, indicating a rise in lake level. This could in part be explained by climatic changes, but is likely to be due to impeded drainage as the outlet in the northern end became choked by developing carr. Subsequently the north and the west developed *Eriophorum* as did the mire at Elan Valley, though here the carr survived around the edges. In recent times these regions have been cut for peat and have regenerated once more, hence their complex stratigraphy. The rejuvenated lake in the south east continued its existence for some time, but became exceedingly dystrophic, its sediments being an organic gel-mud with pollen grains almost the only recognisable remains. This condition was due to a very low nutrient input, hence a low productivity. Its eventual colonisation took place not by reedswamp vegetation but by a floating mat of acid tolerant plants including *Carex rostrata, Menyanthes trifoliata* and *Sphagnum cuspidatum* which spread across the surface of the lake from the edges, eventually forming a complete floating surface on which further bog vegetation could develop.

Thus the stratigraphy at this site shows a layer of water beneath the surface mat, below which are lake sediments. Such a course of development could not be deduced from the present vegetation, which resembles that of many other mire types. This type of succession (see Chapter 3) is not common in Britain, but is more frequent in Continental Europe and in the eastern United States[22, 23].

These three examples of stratigraphic sequences in mires in the

United Kingdom may serve to demonstrate the importance of such studies for the understanding of present day mire vegetation and the successional processes which literally underlie it. A splendid example of the way in which work on peat stratigraphy has overturned entrenched theories on mire origins is the case of the Norfolk Broads[24]. It was believed that these mires and waterways were of an entirely natural origin until work by Lambert and Jennings showed that many of the Broads were fringed by steep sided banks of peat. These had resulted from a vast medieval peat cutting industry which had excavated the Broads and abandoned them as they filled with water.

There are many such instances in which stratigraphical studies have helped to elucidate problems peculiar to specific sites, yet it is surprising how little information has been extracted from stratigraphical studies to improve our knowledge of the dynamic processes involved in hydroseral succession. Most accounts of the vegetational sequences in hydroseres (e.g. Tansley[25]) are based upon the assumption that the spatial arrangement of vegetational communities around an area of open water reflects the temporal succession of communities in mire development. Often this is undoubtedly true, but there are frequently complications in such surface arrangements of vegetation which confuses the situation. The detailed study of peat stratigraphy would seem to be a far more reliable approach to an understanding of sequential development of mires. Walker[26] has recently collated much of the available information from stratigraphical studies and has shown the following types of sequence which occur most commonly in three types of basin.

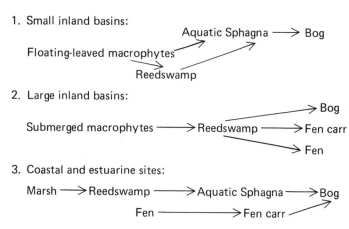

1. Small inland basins:

                        Aquatic Sphagna ⟶ Bog

    Floating-leaved macrophytes

               Reedswamp

2. Large inland basins:

                                           ⟶ Bog

    Submerged macrophytes ⟶ Reedswamp ⟶ Fen carr

                                           ⟶ Fen

3. Coastal and estuarine sites:

    Marsh ⟶ Reedswamp ⟶ Aquatic Sphagna ⟶ Bog

                 Fen ⟶ Fen carr

These sequences demonstrate several significant facts. In the first place they show a diversity of sequence which is far greater than the surface studies of hydroseres have indicated. In the second place they show that certain types of vegetation which we find on mire surfaces appear to be overlooked in stratigraphical studies, for example the tussocky sedge communities which are often found intermixed with carr and which have permanent standing water around the tussocks. The dominant plants in such communities are often *Carex paniculata, C. appropinquata* or *C. acutiformis* and the tussocks are sometimes invaded by tree seedlings, e.g. *Betula* or *Alnus* which find slightly more oxygenated situations there[27]. Such communities are so frequent on the surface of mires it is difficult to believe that they have not existed in the past. Undoubtedly they have gone unrecognised in stratigraphical studies.

A further point to emerge from these studies is that there is no stratigraphical sequence in which oak woodland can be shown to have developed as a result of hydroseral succession. Tansley's assumption that this vegetation type represented the climax of the hydrosere is thus not proved, although occasional *Quercus robur* trees may be found in mature carrs.

The surface vegetation of most mires exhibits varying degrees of heterogeneity and pattern, and detailed examination of lateral variation in peat stratigraphy has indicated that this pattern may be reflected in the peat deposit. For example, early in this century von Post and Sernander[28] described peat deposits which contained evidence of the hummock and hollow vegetation types which were preserved in the peat and could be clearly detected on exposed faces. This led them to propose a cyclic succession within the peat whereby each hummock grew more slowly as it was raised above the water table whereas peat growth in the hollows accelerated. This process, they suggested, would lead to the hollows building into hummocks and the hummocks being left as hollows, after which the roles were reversed. In the peat, lens-shaped, unhumified deposits alternated with dark, well humified bands. This type of sequence has been termed 'regeneration complex'.

More recent work in Ireland by Walker and Walker[29] has suggested that a strict alternation of hummock and hollow does not always occur. In their profiles the positions of the main hummocks remains constant and the pools between them expand and contract periodically. A similar sequence has been found at Claish Moss, Argyll, where the hummocks and pools are arranged in an eccentric manner (following the surface contours, (see Figure 6.7). Faegri and Iversen[10] point out that in the classical regeneration cycle, *Sphagnum fuscum* is an important contributor to the peat, whereas this does not occur in the Irish sections. How-

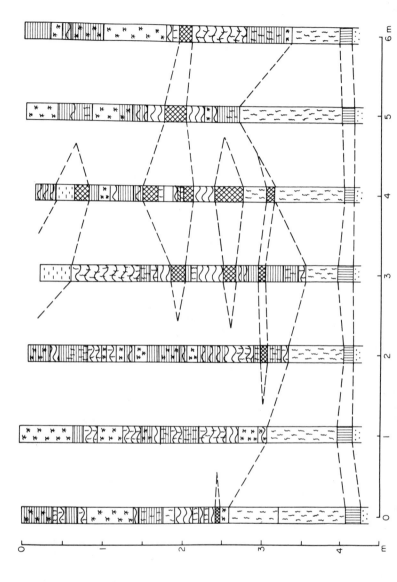

Figure 6.7. Stratigraphic profile of a transect at Claish Moss, Argyll. Symbols as in Figure 6.5. In addition, asterisks = Rhacomitrium lanuginosum peat. Dotted lines are used to link the basal peats and the pool systems in the upper peat profile

152

ever, this species does occur at the Argyll site, so this cannot be the only factor accounting for observed differences (see Chapter 2).

STRATIGRAPHY AND CLIMATE

Many people have looked to the domed mires of western Europe for stratigraphical evidence of past climatic changes. It is to be expected that these structures should be sensitive to such changes since their continued growth is dependent upon the maintenance of high precipitation/evaporation ratios. If the bog growth rate did vary with changes in this ratio, then such variations would be reflected in the degree of humification of the peat formed (i.e. in the time taken to reach the sulphide zone). A German stratigrapher, C.A. Weber, first described the widespread occurrence of an abrupt change from a dark, well humified *Sphagnum* peat to a light, unhumified one at a few metres depth in the domed mires in much of northwest Europe[30]. He called this change the 'grenzhorizont', which means literally 'boundary horizon'. In Germany the older, darker peat often contains pine stumps and *Calluna,* indicating drier conditions on the bog surface prior to the grenz. The bogs during this period may have become so reduced in growth rate that they could be considered as in the 'standstill' phase as described by Osvald[31].

In Scandinavia, the botanists Blytt and Sernander divided the postglacial into five climatically distinct periods on the basis of stratigraphical changes, e.g. the invasion of bogs by pine. These periods are as follows, beginning with the youngest,

Subatlantic	(cold and wet)
Subboreal	(warm and dry)
Atlantic	(warm and wet)
Boreal	(warm and dry)
Preboreal	(subarctic)

The grenz of Weber was considered to mark the change from the subboreal to subatlantic period, a change favouring bog growth.

Climate, however, varies with a number of factors, e.g. altitude and geographical proximity to the sea, and whereas a bog in one climatic regime may respond to a climatic change, in other areas they may not. Conway[32] has developed von Post's concept of threshold climates, e.g. moisture levels which must be exceeded before a bog responds in its overall growth rate. Such a concept accounts for local variations in the time at which a stratigraphical feature such as the grenz occurs. Usually the radiocarbon date of this horizon falls close to 500 B.C.

It became evident fairly early in this century, however, that the single stratigraphical change described by Weber was not adequate to account for the numerous examples of this type of change found over northern

Europe. Granlund[33], working in southern Sweden, described five such features which he termed 'recurrence surfaces'. These have been dated as follows,

RY	I	1200 A.D.
RY	II	400 A.D.
RY	III	600 B.C. (= Weber's grenz)
RY	IV	1200 B.C.
RY	V	2300 B.C.

At each of these dates, he contended, a climatic change involving increased wetness caused bogs to grow actively following a standstill phase. This concept is based upon the belief that within a given set of climatic conditions there is a limit to the height which a raised bog can attain and climatic change is required if further growth is to occur. This assumption is now open to doubt.

The picture was made even more complex by the work of Nilsson[34], who identified a total of nine such recurrence surfaces in Scania, Sweden. The description of such surfaces, which are both less obvious and more localised in occurrence, needs to be interpreted in the light of Conway's threshold concept; the changes in one region may not be present in another.

Overbeck[34] and his colleagues in Germany continued the task of dating recurrence surfaces and demonstrated a variation in dates which is difficult to explain. The main concentration of dates was at about 700 B.C., 100 B.C. and A.D. 600. The first and last dates may correspond to Granlund's RY III and RY II respectively. The dates Overbeck quotes were obtained from samples at the recurrence surfaces of different bogs, but one might well ask whether a horizon is synchronous over a single bog. Schneekloth[35] has recently investigated this problem in exposed peat faces in German bogs. In these he shows that there is considerable variation in the radiocarbon dates of recurrence surfaces of any one bog, for example at Gifhorner Moor his eight dates span a total of 1100 years, from 400 B.C. to 700 A.D. We are led to the conclusion that the periods of renewed, active bog growth may well differ from one part of a bog to another. Thus the pattern of growth phases in a bog may well prove to be as complex as the patterning of the peat forming vegetation itself. If this is so, then many so-called recurrence surfaces may be dismissed as an expression of local drainage features in the course of the history of the mire.

The study of peat stratigraphy solves some problems of mire history and vegetational succession, but it tends to raise far more problems than it solves. However, further work may serve to elucidate some of these.

REFERENCES

1. OVERBECK, F. 'Studien zur Hochmoorentwicklung in Niedersachsen und die Bestimmung der Humifizierung bei stratigraph-pollenanalytischen Mooruntersuchungen.' *Planta,* **35,** 1 (1947).
2. DICKSON, C.A. 'The study of plant macrofossils in British Quaternary deposits.' In *Stuaies in the Vegetational History of the British·Isles.* Ed. WALKER, D. and WEST, R.G. Cambridge, 233 (1970).
3. GODWIN, H. *The History of the British Flora.* Cambridge (1956).
4. JANE, F.W. *The Structure of Wood.* London (1956).
5. RICHARDSON, D.H.S. and GREEN, B.H. 'A subfossil lichen' *Lichenologist,* **3,** 89 (1965).
6. SERNANDER, R. 'Subfossile Flechten.' *Flora, Jena,* **112,** 703 (1918).
7. KLEMENT, O. 'Über subfossile Flechtensporen.' *Schr. naturw. Ver., Sch.-Holst.* **26,** 113 (1955).
8. WATTS, W.A. 'Interglacial deposits at Kilbeg and Newtown, Co. Waterford.' *Proc. R. Irish Acad.* B. **60,** 79 (1959).
9. BLOCK, W.C. 'Recovery of mites from peat and mineral soils using a new flotation method.' *J. Anim. Ecol.* **36,** 323 (1967).
10. FAEGRI, K. and IVERSEN, J. *Textbook of Pollen Analysis.* Oxford (1964).
11. ERDTMAN, G., BERGLUND, B. and PRAGLOWSKI, J. 'An introduction to a Scandinavian pollen flora.' *Grana Palynol.* **2** (3) 3 (1961).
12. ANDREW, R. 'The Cambridge pollen reference collection.' In *Studies in The Vegetational History of the British Isles.* Ed. WALKER, D. and WEST, R.G. Cambridge, 225 (1970).
13. HIRST, J.M. STEDMAN, O.J. and HOGG, W.H. 'Long-distance spore transport: methods of measurement, vertical spore profiles and the detection of immigrant spores.' *J. gen. Microbiol.* **48,** 329 (1967).
14. STEWART, J.M. and DURNO, S.E. 'Structural variations in peat.' *New Phytol.* **68,** 167 (1969).
15. TALLIS, J.H. and BIRKS, H.J.B. 'The past and present distribution of *Scheuchzeria palustris* L. in Europe.' *J. Ecol.* **53,** 287 (1965).
16. WEST, R.G. *Pleistocene Geology and Biology.* London. 99 (1968).
17. MOORE, P.D. and CHATER, E.H. 'Studies in the vegetational history of mid-Wales. I. The post-glacial period in Cardiganshire.' *New Phytol.* **68,** 183 (1969).
18. MOORE, P.D. 'Studies in the vegetational history of mid-Wales. II. The late-glacial period in Cardiganshire.' *New Phytol.* **69,** 363 (1970).
19. PIGOTT, C.D. and PIGOTT, M.E. 'Late-glacial and post-glacial deposits at Malham, Yorkshire.' *New Phytol.* **62,** 317 (1963).
20. GREEN, B.H. 'Factors influencing the spatial and temporal distribution of *Sphagnum imbricatum* Hornsch. ex Russ, in the British Isles.' *J. Ecol.* **56,** 47 (1968).
21. MOORE, P.D. and BECKETT, P.J. 'Vegetation and development of Llyn, a Welsh mire.' *Nature, Lond.* **231,** 363 (1971).
22. CONWAY, V.M. 'The bogs of central Minnesota.' *Ecol. Monogr.* **19,** 173 (1949).
23. DEEVEY, E.S. 'Bogs.' *Scientific American.* October (1958).
24. LAMBERT, J.M., JENNINGS, J.N., SMITH, C.T., GREEN, C. and HUTCHINSON, J.N. *The Making of the Broads.* London (1960).
25. TANSLEY, A.G. *The British Islands and their Vegetation.* Cambridge (1939).
26. WALKER, D. 'Direction and rate in some British post-glacial hydroseres.'

In *Studies in the Vegetational History of the British Isles.* Ed. WALKER, D. and WEST, R.G., Cambridge. 117 (1970).

27. LAMBERT, J.M. 'The Vegetation of Broadland.' In *The Broads.* E.A. Ellis, London (1965).
28. VON POST, L. and SERNANDER, R. 'Pflanzenphysiognomische Studien auf Torfmooren in Närke.' Geologkongressen Guide Excursion A.7 (1910).
29. WALKER, D. and WALKER, P.M. 'Stratigraphic evidence of regeneration in some Irish bogs.' *J. Ecol.* **49**, 169 (1961).
30. WEBER, C.A. 'Uber die Moore mit besonderer Berncksichtigung der zwischen Unterweser und Unterelbe liegenden.' *Jb. Männer v. Morgenstern,* **3**, 3 (1960).
31. OSVALD, H. 'Die Vegetation des Hochmoores Komosse.' *Svensk. vaxtsociol. sällsk.* Landl. I. (1923).
32. CONWAY, U.M. 'Von Post's work on climatic rhythms.' *New Phytol,* **47**, 220 (1948).
33. GRANLUND, E. 'De svenska högmossarnas geologi.' *Sveriges geol. unders.* Scr. C.**26**, 373 (1932).
34. OVERBECK, F., MÜNNICH, K.O., ALETSEE, L. and AVERDIECK, F.R. 'Das Alter des "Grenzhorizontes" nordentscher Hochmoore nach Radiocarbon-Datierungen.' *Flora, Jena,* **145**, 37 (1957).
35. SCHNEEKLOTH, H. 'The significance of the limiting horizon for the chronostratigraphy of raised bogs: results of a critical investigation.' *Proc. 3rd Int. Peat Congress, Quebec.* 116 (1968).

156

Chapter Seven

The Microscopic Components of Peat

In Chapter 6 we considered the macroscopic fossil material in peat deposits and considered the usefulness of this component of peat in building up a picture of the successional processes in operation during the development of a mire. It is the physical size of these macrofossil which, by reducing the chances of their being carried any great distance, makes them useful in tracing the vegetation which occupied the site in past times. The smaller, microfossil component of peats does not necessarily suffer such limitations of transportation, therefore its derivation need not be local. This means that the interpretation of microfossil assemblages is a far more complex matter than was the case with the macrofossils; however it does permit deductions to be made about regional as well as local vegetational changes.

POLLEN GRAINS

By far the most useful microfossils in peats from the ecological standpoint are the pollen grains of angiosperm and gymnosperm plants together with the spores of pteridophytes and some bryophytes. Fungal spores are often present in considerable quantities in peats, but so far these have received little attention from palaeoecologists.

Botanically, pollen and spores are quite distinct. Pollen grains represent the reduced male gametophyte generation in the flowering plants (angiosperms and gymnosperms). In the bryophytes and most pteridophytes the gametophyte is photosynthetic and free living, usually dwelling on the surface of the soil. These independent gametophytes arise as a result of the germination of a spore. Pollen grains and spores have one important feature in common and that is their requirement for transportation from one place to another, in the case of pollen grains to a stigma of the same species, and in the case of spores, to a suitable site for germination and establishment of the gametophyte. Many pollen grains and spores show structural adaptations giving them selective advantages for such transportation. Both pollen grains and spores arise as a result of meiotic division of a diploid mother cell. This produces a tetrad of haploid cells which may or may not split up into single grains or spores (see Figure 7.1). Many

157

spores on splitting into individuals retain a Y shaped (trilete) mark on their surface (e.g. *Pteridium* and *Sphagnum*) which is the scar from their mutual attachment in the tetrad. This is not normally found in pollen grains.

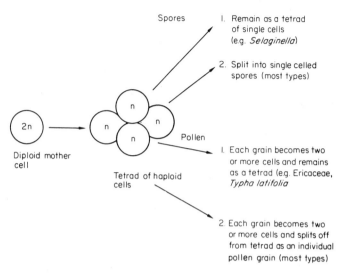

Figure 7.1. Formation of pollen grains and spores.

The development of the wall of the pollen grain is complex. It begins formation during the tetrad stage and involves the secretion of cellulose, lipoprotein and a resistant material termed [by Heslop-Harrison[1]] 'protosporopollenin'. In grains which are released from the tetrad, the free spore period is accompanied by further developments in the wall structure involving the accretion of sporopollenin and the formation of an inner cellulose wall, the intine. The structure of the outer coat (exine) is far more complex than that of the intine, and the sculpturing of this coat begins very early in wall formation, during the tetrad phase.

The material sporopollenin which is involved in the structure of the exine is of considerable interest because of its great resistance to decay processes. Chemically sporopollenin is thought to be an oxidative polymer of carotenoids and carotenoid esters and some suggest that it is an important component of the organic materials surviving in Precambrian rocks[2], perhaps as much as 3×10^9 years old. Its resistance to microbial attack allows the survival of the pollen exine and the coats of spores under the conditions of peat formation. Survival is even possible in soils where conditions are acid[3], and Iversen has reported mor humus accumulation in woodland which is almost pure pollen[4], most other material having decomposed.

The sculpturing of pollen and spores, together with the arrangement of such features as grooves and pores, is valuable in their identification. Many types can be identified to the level of species as a result of these features, but as yet many can only be assigned to a genus or even a family. The level of identification possible is constantly improving as more and more taxonomic work is carried out on pollen grains and as techniques such as scanning electron microscopy are applied to their study[5]. A number of keys are available for pollen identification, but the most useful general key is supplied by Faegri and Iversen[6].

POLLEN IN PEAT

The discovery of pollen grains surviving in peat and the realisation of their potential for the study of past vegetation was due to the Scandinavian botanist Lennart von Post. He took a few cubic millimetres of peat and boiled the sample in 10% potassium hydroxide solution over a spirit lamp on a slide whilst holding it with a clothes peg! In this way the unsaturated organic colloids (humic acids) were removed and the pollen grains and spores remained undamaged. This method of pollen extraction is still used with minor modifications, such as the use of a centrifuge for washing the sample and a sieve to remove large fragments. Where deposits are rich in cellulose, e.g. in moss leaves and root cells, a more severe method of pollen concentration may be necessary, such as the acetolysis technique developed by Erdtman[7]. In this the sample is boiled in a mixture of glacial acetic acid and concentrated sulphuric acid for one minute. Cellulose is destroyed by this process, but pollen exines are not if the boiling proceeds for no longer than a minute. The presence of siliceous matter in a deposit may demand boiling in hydrofluoric acid, but the pollen exines remain undamaged.

Thus it is possible to extract pollen and spores from a sample of peat and to identify the bulk of such an extract at least to generic level. However, it is not possible to express these data in absolute terms unless one has knowledge of the rate of peat formation. We may have data concerning the number of pollen grains per unit volume of peat, but unless we know the number of years taken to form that depth of peat we cannot express the results in terms of numbers of pollen per unit area of mire surface per year. As we saw in Chapter 6, the rate of peat formation is very variable, both as a function of climatic change and as a result of local environmental factors, hence even a large number of radiocarbon dates may not enable one to express pollen data in absolute terms. As a result one has to express each species as a percentage of the whole. In practice it has become conventional to express such percentages in terms of arboreal pollen simply because the arboreal pollen usually comes from outside the mire system and hence the results are not confused by local fluctuations in pollen input. This system has the grave disadvantage, however, of making each tree species dependent upon every other, for if one species is reduced in its absolute pollen input all other species will be artificially inflated as a result, simply because the total tree pollen must remain at 100%. Similarly if all trees become less common but retain their proportions with respect to one another then the change will not be shown in the tree pollen percentages. This can be overcome by tracing the tree pollen : non-tree pollen ratio.

Sampling errors in pollen analysis are extremely large. They enter in at four stages:

1. The selection of a sample site on the mire
2. The removal of a peat sample at a given level
3. Subsampling of the extracted pollen to produce slides
4. Counting only a sample of the pollen grains on a slide.

These errors can be reduced by duplication of samples at each stage and by enlarging the number of pollen grains counted. However, this requires greater time expenditure and a balance must be reached. In general the counting of intermediate samples often provides an indication of whether samples are adequate, except in cases where rapid changes are occurring.

Where more than one pollen diagram has been produced for a site, they are often in quite close agreement, though this is not the case if the vegetation of each side of a mire differs substantially. For example Turner showed that pollen diagrams from different parts of Tregaron Bog in mid-Wales differed with the various land use patterns and histories of the surrounding areas[8]. Pollen analyses, therefore, are normally repeatable and are therefore considered to be valid representations of the various pollen proportions at a given peat level. However, the application of statistical techniques to give added precision to the deductions made from such analyses is still in its infancy.

THE ORIGINS OF FOSSIL POLLEN

Once we are contented that we have a reasonable estimate of the relative proportions of pollen types at various depths within a deposit, we are faced with the problem of analysing the origins of such pollen. Tauber[9] has suggested that there are three main sources of pollen in a peat deposit. These are illustrated in Figure 7.2.

1. Pollen washed from the atmosphere by rain and possibly descending from a considerable altitude.
2. Pollen descending slowly from the air under the influence of gravity, having originated as a result of drifting upwards through tree canopies.
3. Pollen which moves laterally through the trunk space of a forest before settling upon the site.

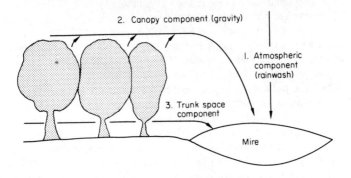

Figure 7.2.   Tauber model of pollen input into a mire.

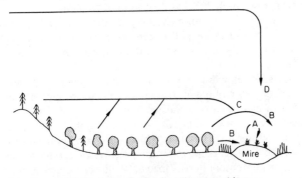

Figure 7.3.   Geographical origins of a fossil pollen assemblage.

When considering the vegetation from which pollen has been derived, one is really concerned with the distance over which pollen has travelled. Figure 7.3 illustrates the possible origins of pollen in terms of the vegetation producing it. These are:

161

A. Local mire plants growing within a radius of a few metres of the site sampled
B. Mire vegetation from periferal regions, which is possibly quite different from the immediate local vegetation, e.g. carr and fen vegetation around the edge of domed mires
C. Regional vegetation, its extent being dependent upon local land forms and topography together with prevailing air currents. It is likely to be of the order of several kilometres in radius
D. Vegetation growing considerable distances from the site (up to hundreds of kilometres).

The two schemes may be related as follows:
1. Rainwash pollen will be of type D and possibly C
2. Gravitational pollen will be mainly type C
3. Trunk space pollen is likely to be of type B and may not reach the centre of large mires. Tauber was dealing with essentially wooded areas, hence he gives no equivalent of type A.

Thus the pollen which we extract from a peat sample can have been derived from a considerable variety of sources. It would be useful to separate these sources, if such were possible, but this is rarely the case. Tauber estimates that the rainwash component may be 20% of the total pollen; the canopy component will vary with the distance from the edge of the forest. For a site 1 km from the forest edge, 50% of the pollen is estimated to come from over 10–11 km away. Similarly the trunk space component becomes greater as one approaches the forest edge, perhaps reaching 80% within 100 m of the edge.

The long distance component may be particularly misleading. For example, *Pinus* and *Picea* pollen can reach values of 20% of the total pollen in the Canadian arctic, 400 km north of their distribution limit [10].

The differential wind transport of pollen grains also needs to be considered. Wind pollinated species normally produce a low density pollen which can be carried considerable distances. The pollen of insect pollinated types is usually heavier and hence sinks to the ground more rapidly, i.e. closer to its source. This offers some opportunity for the separation of local and regional components of a pollen rain. It also means that entomophilous species will be underrepresented in comparison with anemophilous types. Wind pollinated species also tend to produce greater quantities of pollen than insect pollinated types, which also results in overrepresentation of the former. The outcome of this is that even if we were able to separate out the various pollen components efficiently (which we cannot) one still cannot assume that the abundance of the pollen of a species reflects the abundance of that species, especially where all abundances are expressed on a proportional basis.

HABITAT RECONSTRUCTION

We have seen that many difficulties attend the translation of a pollen count into a picture of the vegetation giving rise to that pollen. A final problem to be considered is the separation of pollen assemblages into ecologically meaningful groups representative of the plant communities from which the pollen originated. Vegetation is not a homogeneous blanket of uniformly spaced individuals, but is more like a mosaic of communities reflecting the diversity of the natural environment. Whether such communities should be regarded as discrete units or as a multidimensional continuum does not alter the fact of vegetational heterogeneity and it is this fact which the palaeoecologist must bear in mind when trying to reconstruct the vegetation of the past.

A number of problems arise when we attempt to split a pollen assemblage into its ecological components. The first of these is the degree of precision possible in pollen identification. As we mentioned earlier, many pollen types cannot be taken beyond the level of family. This is a problem which may be overcome in time as more research is carried out, but at present it represents a considerable obstacle to the full understanding of the pollen record. For example, it is difficult to subdivide further the family Gramineae, the grasses. An exception is provided by the cereal pollen grains which are often much larger than most other grass types. Faegri and Iversen[6] have devised a key by which subdivision into groups of genera is possible, but it does not overcome the problem of the separation of ecological groups, e.g. their *'Festuca* group' includes genera such as *Phalaris, Molinia, Lolium, Holcus* and *Agrostis*. Between them, species of these genera cover a very wide range of habitats. Indeed even within a given genus one may find species of very different ecological requirements, e.g. *Deschampsia,* hence pollen grains need to be identified to species level before firm conclusions regarding habitats can be made.

Even where identification is possible to the level of species one needs to make two basic assumptions before one can extrapolate from these data to habitat reconstruction. In the first place one must assume that the ecology of species in the past is the same as that of its living counterparts. It is difficult to justify such an assumption but it is also difficult to disprove it. Some have regarded the questioning of such an assumption as tantamount to disbelief in the uniformity of nature. However, biological material is notoriously variable and its variations are subject to the changing pressures of natural selection, so there is no

163

basic reason why the assumption should not be questioned and certainly its tenuousness should be kept in mind. In the second place there is the possibility of ecotypic variation within a species which might result in different genetic strains of a species having totally different habitat requirements. Such situations are well documented for a number of living species, e.g. *Festuca ovina*[11], and have been invoked by some authors to explain anomalies in the past behaviour of species, e.g. *Pinus sylvestris*[12] and *Sphagnum imbricatum*[13]. There is always the possibility that ecotypes have existed in the past which are now extinct, hence the testing of any such hypothesis is impossible. Perhaps it is this fact, i.e. one's inability to prove or disprove such an hypothesis, which makes palaeoecologists rather shy of taking up this position.

In trying to reconstruct past habitats one is also faced with the possibility that the precise equivalent of the community no longer exists today. This is a familiar problem to those palaeoecologists concerned with the distant past, but it is often overlooked by those working on the Flandrian period, the last 10 000 years or so since the close of the last glaciation. We tend to argue back from our present experience of plant communities, yet we have every reason to believe that certain situations in the past cannot have a modern equivalent. For example, arctic tundra conditions once existed at low altitude in southern Britain. We cannot regard the tundra of the high latitudes, with its vastly different season and day length, as ecologically equivalent. Again, there was a time when the climate of Britain was warm enough for the growth of temperate forest, yet such vegetation was still far south of this area and slowly migrating north. It is difficult to envisage the type of vegetation resulting from such a situation in anything but the most general of terms.

Similar problems are presented by the reconstruction of the primeval forest before man became a dominant influence upon its structure and composition together with the understanding of communities and habitats under conditions of primitive agriculture.

Despite all of these problems, much research has gone into the unravelling of past environments and the study of pollen assemblages in peat deposits has probably contributed more to our knowledge of these environments than any other single discipline. There are several books which are devoted to the collation of results from such research, the most important being Sir Harry Godwin's *The History of the British Flora*[14]. More recently Dr. Winifred Pennington has written a concise account of climatic and vegetational changes in her book *The History of British Vegetation*[15]. The existence of these admirable accounts makes it superfluous to attempt any comprehensive review of our current state of knowledge, however it may prove valuable to illustrate some of the principles and problems enunciated in the first part of this chapter by considering a particular case history.

UPLAND MID-WALES — A CASE HISTORY

As an example of the type of results obtained from pollen analytical work we shall take two sites in the upland area of mid-Wales. The first is the Elan Valley Bog[16], a mire situated in a valley of 384m (1260 ft) altitude at the watershed of the Cambrian mountains, and the second is a blanket mire site on a plateau close to the summit of Plynlimmon[17,18], the highest point in central Wales.

The Elan Valley Bog was mentioned in Chapter 6 as an example of the stratigraphic succession in a mire developed over a lake basin under ombrotrophic conditions. A profile of the mire was given in Figure 6.5. Figures 7.4 and 7.5 show the results of pollen analysis of a core from the Elan Valley mire at the point marked 'X' on the stratigraphical profile. The peat stratigraphy at this point is summarised in the column on the left hand side of Figure 7.4 where the mire can be seen to overlie lake sediments (see Chapter 6 for stratigraphic symbols).

The pollen diagram itself shows the variation in the proportions of different pollen types with depth. It is represented in a histogram form, although such diagrams are occasionally blocked in completely, the sampling points being joined by straight lines. Such a method of presentation is not entirely satisfactory for similar reasons to those involved in drawing up peat profiles (see Chapter 6). When two sampling points are joined together in a graph one is assuming that points at intermediate depth are intermediate in value. This assumption is totally unjustified.

The column next to the depth scale in Figure 7.4 is labelled TPFI, which stands for *total pollen frequency index*. This is an inverse expression of the abundance of pollen in the sample analysed, the higher the index the less abundant the pollen per unit volume of peat. The abundance of pollen will be dependent upon the rate of pollen deposition from the atmosphere and the rate of peat formation. The usefulness of the expression is that when the vegetational composition is stable (not undergoing rapid change) one may be justified in assuming a constant rate of pollen input ('pollen rain'). Under such circumstances any change in the TPFI will be due to changes in the rate of peat deposition. This, as we saw in Chapter 6, could reflect changes in peat forming vegetation, in local environmental conditions, e.g. drainage, or in the precipitation—evaporation ratio of the climate. The extrapolation

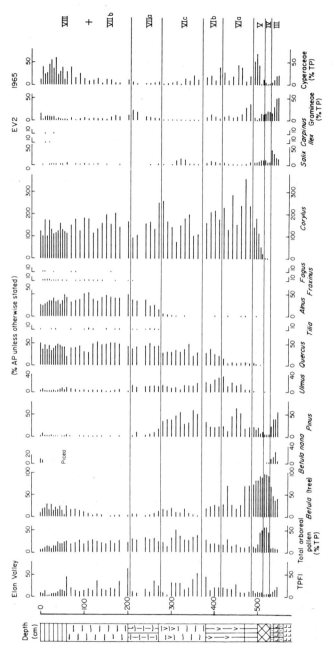

Figure 7.4.   Pollen diagram from the Elan Valley Bog (after New Phytologist).

166

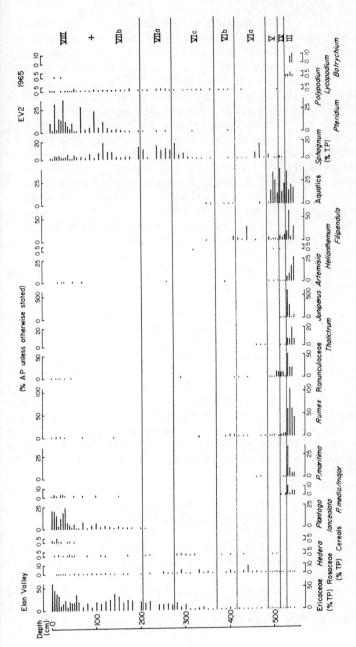

Figure 7.5. Pollen diagram from the Elan Valley Bog.

167

is somewhat tenuous, especially since it depends on an assumption of constant pollen rain; also the factor of peat compression is not accounted for. However in situations where there is a sudden rise in TPFI without changes in overall pollen proportions or peat stratigraphy, the index may be a useful one.

The remaining columns in the diagrams show changes in the relative proportions of various pollen types with peat depth, all expressed as a percentage of arboreal pollen except for Gramineae, Cyperaceae, Ericaceae and Rosaceae. The reason for excluding these from the conventional expression is because species of these families are the most abundant plants in the peat forming vegetation, e.g. *Phragmites, Molinia, Eriophorum* spp. *Calluna, Erica* and *Potentilla erecta*. Pollen of these types is therefore abundant and of only local significance; the same applies to the spore of *Sphagnum*. These types are therefore expressed and interpreted separately from the remaining types, most of which can be regarded as originating outside the mire system.

The horizontal lines on the pollen diagrams represent the division of the sequence into 'zones', which are temporal periods defined by the relative pollen proportions and having some degree of homogeneity within itself. The zones used here are those originally proposed by Godwin[14] and labelled III to VIII (zones I and II are present in the lake sediments but are not considered here[19]). Godwin's zones were originally defined in East Anglia, which makes their application to upland Wales rather difficult. In using the same zone notation one may be guilty of misrepresentation[12], for this conveys the suggestion that the zones are contemporaneous with those of East Anglia, which is not proven. There is a case, therefore, for the construction of a new zonation system in regions which might have differed in their climates and therefore in their vegetation during past times, despite the increased complexity involved in the correlation of results. Such complexity is real and can easily be neglected under the panacea of the conventional zonation system.

However, if we take the zones as they stand at this site and do not pay too great attention to their labelling, then we can begin to interpret the pollen changes in terms of changing vegetation.

Zone III

This is represented by a grey lake clay underlying the mire and is typified by very low arboreal pollen when expressed as a percentage of the total pollen. The arboreal pollen present comes largely from birch and pine, and it is possible to separate from the birch pollen that of *Betula nana*, the dwarf birch, which is a prostrate tree of arctic—alpine distribution. Pine pollen is frequent, but one must bear in mind the

168

inflation of its value by the method of expression as percentage arboreal pollen, and also the possibilities of long distance transport of this pollen.

Figure 7.5 (the continuation of Figure 7.4) shows that certain pollen types are abundant in this zone, particularly *Juniperus, Rumex* (sorrel) and *Plantago maritima* (sea plantain).

In interpreting these data one must conceive of a landscape with few trees except for scattered birch, with a scrub of dwarf birch and juniper. It is generally believed now that pine was not present in Britain during this period, but its pollen reached such sites by long distance transport. Species such as the plantains and *Artemisia,* together with *Lycopodium* and *Botrychium,* may have contributed to the ground layer of this vegation, being overrepresented in terms of their importance in the vegetation due to their high pollen production and wind-dispersal mechanisms. Types such as *Filipendula* and Ranunculaceae are probably derived from a local marsh community at the margins of the lake.

Thus the vegetation was of open tundra type with few trees. Climatic conditions are likely to have been cold (hence the lack of trees).

Zone IV

This zone is quite different, for arboreal pollen suddenly becomes very abundant and there is an equally sudden diminution in the pollen of other species. In part this latter feature may be a consequence of the former, for most nonarboreal species are expressed relative to arboreal pollen, hence an increase in tree pollen will result in a decrease in the representation of such types.

Within the tree pollen we find that one type, *Betula,* predominates. When this happens one tends to suspect that it is overrepresented for some reason, and an examination of the lake muds of this zone reveals the presence of birch fruits and catkin scales of the species *Betula pubescens.* Here is an example of how macrofossil remains help in the interpretation of microfossils, both in lending precision to the identification and in explaining the very high values of birch. *Betula pubescens* is the birch species normally associated with damp situations and the abundance of macrofossil remains of this species suggests that it was present locally, perhaps around the margins of the shallow lake. This being so, one wonders what type of vegetation covered the hill slopes beyond the immediate vicinity of the lake. It is possible that they were still clothed by tundra, or perhaps by birch woodland. The latter is more likely since even grasses and sedges diminish in this zone, despite their expression as a percentage of total pollen. It is unlikely that woodland other than birch existed or one would expect some other arboreal pollen to find its way into the sediment.

Zone V

During this phase considerable changes were initiated in both the local and the regional vegetation. Within it the allochthonous lake muds give way to autochthonous, telmatic peats, largely of *Carex,* and these changes show up in the pollen diagram by an increase in Cyperaceae pollen and a decrease in that of the 'aquatics' group, which contains submerged and floating hydrophytes such as *Potamogeton, Myriophyllum, Nymphaea,* etc.

Regionally the most marked change is the rising quantity of *Corylus* (hazel) and pine pollen, whilst birch decreases accordingly. The decrease of the latter need not be a genuine one, but simply a statistical artefact as a result of the rise in pine. The total arboreal pollen decreases markedly in this zone, which could be a result of the demise of local birch woodland at the mire margins, or could be due to the increasing abundance of hazel.

Thus interpretation becomes very complex at this stage, but it is reasonable to suppose that both hazel and pine invaded the environs of the mire at this stage and that the spread of the former was particularly rapid, perhaps at the expense of some birch. The development of birch and hazel woodland indicates that the climate must have been warmer at this stage than during zone III. It is difficult to determine how much warmer because although temperate broadleaf woodland was not fully established, this may not have been the result of climatic limitations. Even if the climatic change had been a rapid one it would have taken some time for the forest to migrate north from southern Europe. Thus the sequence of woodland species may be a reflection of their relative migration rates rather than the rate of climatic change.

Zone VI

This zone is subdivided into three subzones, a, b and c. In subzone VIa hazel reaches its highest values, oak and elm make their first appearance in any quantity, birch decreases and pine increases, Within this subzone elm pollen is more abundant than that of oak, which is a definitive feature.

Hazel is known to produce large quantities of pollen, but the widespread dispersal of this pollen becomes restricted if the hazel is growing as an understorey below a forest canopy. The abundance of hazel pollen in this subzone may be a result of an open canopy situation in which oak, elm and pine trees emerged from dense stands of hazel. The paucity of open habitat species suggests that little ground was free of tree or shrub cover.

170

In subzone VIb oak and elm continue to expand and oak becomes the most abundantly represented tree. Hazel pollen becomes less frequent, which could indicate the closing of the forest canopy. This occurrence would restrict much hazel pollen to the 'trunkspace' region of Tauber and cause it to be less well represented in peat deposits. Thus the decrease in the relative proportions of hazel pollen in this subzone need not represent an actual decrease in the abundance of hazel. In addition, if the total arboreal pollen is increasing as is suggested by its proportional representation in the pollen assemblage, then the values of nonarboreal pollen which are expressed relative to tree pollen will automatically fall. Again this need not represent an actual decrease in the species under examination, but is an artificial result of using proportional expressions.

Towards the close of subzone VIb the peat stratigraphy changes from reedswamp/carr peat to *Eriophorum/Calluna* peat. This indicates that conditions were becoming more ombrotrophic. A decline in the pollen of Gramineae occurs at this transition, probably due to the decrease in *Phragmites; Filipendula* disappears during the zone, which means that even the mire margins under rheotrophic conditions must have become poor in terms of nutrients. The progressive leaching of the surrounding soils is a likely cause of this.

Subzone VIc is marked by a considerable increase in pine, and decrease in birch. This upsurge of pine is of considerable interest since it is a very common feature of pollen diagrams from northern and western Britain but does not occur in the southeast[12]. It would be of considerable interest to know whether the pine pollen is derived locally or regionally, i.e. whether the pine trees are invading the mire site or its immediate vicinity or whether the surrounding forests are increasing in their content of pine. In fact it is difficult to determine which of these processes is occurring. Pine wood is found in the stratigraphy at this level, which may indicate that the tree is of local importance only. However, this is not invariably true of all sites where a zone VIc pine peak occurs.

Zone VIIa

This is marked by a sudden increase in alder (*Alnus*) and a decrease in pine. This feature is common to most English and Welsh pollen diagrams. *Tilia* (lime) pollen also makes its first appearance at this level. There is no evidence of alder being present locally, hence these changes must be considered as of regional significance. Such changes in the general composition of woodlands are thought to indicate that climatic conditions were becoming warmer and wetter.

Increased wetness may be the cause of stratigraphic changes

occurring at this level, since *Phragmites* reinvades the area from which it was earlier eliminated. The full stratigraphic profile (Figure 6.3) shows that this was a local extension of the marginal *Phragmites* into the centre of the mire. Such an extension could have been caused by hydrological changes involving increased stream output and downwash, particularly down the steep eastern slopes onto the surface of the mire. A temporary reversal to minerotrophic conditions would have favoured the spread of *Phragmites.* Gramineae pollen can be seen to increase through the zone.

Also increasing in this zone is the abundance of *Sphagnum* spores, again a possible indication of increased mire wetness.

Zones VIIb and VIII

These two zones were distinguished by Godwin, but are not separable on this diagram. The opening of zone VIIb is marked by a sudden decrease in the pollen of elm and also by the appearance of *Plantago laceolata,* the ribwort plantain. Apart from this, at least during the early stages of this zone, the forest composition remains basically unaltered.

Numerous theories have been advanced to account for the sudden decline in elm pollen[20,21], such as climatic change, disease and selective felling or pollarding of elm by man. The last explanation is now the one which is most generally accepted, despite initial unwillingness on the part of research workers to admit to its feasibility. The selection of elm could have been due to the value of the twigs and bark of this tree as a winter feed for domesticated animals — a practice still carried out in parts of Scandinavia.

From Zone VIIb onwards, then, we have entered a period when human influence began to make its mark upon regional vegetation. Most of the changes in pollen frequencies subsequent to this are explicable directly or indirectly in anthropogenic terms and will be discussed in greater detail in the second example of a pollen diagram later in this chapter. First let us attempt to correlate the pollen zonation system with the climatic periods of Blytt and Sernander (Chapter 6). A tentative correlation is given in Table 7.1, together with radiocarbon datings of the zone boundaries[22,23]. These dates may not be synchronous throughout the country.

Accurate radiocarbon dates are rather difficult to obtain from peat deposits for two main reasons: first, conventional peat sampling equipment does not normally produce a sufficiently large sample at any given level for analysis; and secondly, penetration of roots from plants growing at a later stage in succession may contaminate samples and produce a date which is too young. The validity of radiocarbon dating

172

TABLE 7.1

		} Subatlantic
VIII _____	500 B.C.	
		} Subboreal
VIIb		
_____	3 000 B.C.	
VIIa		} Atlantic
_____	5 500 B.C.	
VI		
_____	7 000 B.C.	} Boreal
V		
_____	7 600 B.C.	
IV		} Preboreal
_____	8 300 B.C.	
I–III		} (Late Weichselian)

as a whole has been in question in recent years and it is now fairly generally agreed that dates before 2 000 years ago require correction to allow for fluctuations in cosmic ray flux. The correction factor becomes larger, i.e. departure from the true date becomes greater, as we go back in time. Thus the radiocarbon dates quoted above may be about 600 years too young at 3 000 B.C., 900 years too young at 5 000 B.C. and so on[24,25].

In order to demonstrate the usefulness of mire pollen analysis for the elucidation of human environmental history we shall now turn from the Elan Valley Bog to an area of blanket mire about 12 km to the north and at an altitude of 564m (1850 ft). As well as being 180m higher

173

than the Elan Valley site, this mire at Plynlimmon is far more exposed on a ridge close to the summit of the mountain. It is therefore likely to receive airborne pollen from a wide region round about.

A pollen diagram and peat profile are given in Figures 7.6 and 7.7. The peat has developed over gently sloping ground and is less than 2m in depth. Its stratigraphy is fairly simple, a basal mor humus layer overlying a fossil podsolised soil, and on top of this a fairly uniform, fibrous peat of *Eriophorum* with occasional *Sphagnum*.

The basal part of the diagram is considered to belong to zone VIIa and there is a clear elm decline which marks the commencement of zone VIIb. Evidence from this and other diagrams in mid-Wales therefore suggests that the shallow blanket peats in this region began their formation at about the time of 'VIIa–VIIb' transition. This may be about 3 000 B.C. Following this, the diagram has been divided into a series of zones labelled A–F on the basis of the pollen profile, changes which are considered to be largely due to local and regional vegetational disturbance at the hand of man.

Zone A

In this zone total arboreal pollen is high, fluctuation in the tree curves are few and minor and weed pollen (particularly *Plantago lanceolata*) is infrequent. The presence of the latter, together with the erratic behaviour of the elm curve, suggest that man is present in the area but having limited effect upon the vegetation. The presence of *Pteridium* (bracken) and *Fraxinus* (ash) may indicate local openings in the forest canopy where these light demanding species could establish themselves. Evidently human populations were low at this time and their demands upon the environment were minimal. Zone A is perhaps to be equated to the Neolithic period.

Zone B

In this zone there are two distinct periods in which the proportion of arboreal pollen falls and when *Plantago*, ruderal (weed) species and *Pteridium* come to small maxima. The coincidence of these changes suggests sudden but temporary clearances being made in the forest which is subsequently allowed to regenerate. This regeneration would appear to be complete after each of these clearance episodes since the arboreal pollen sum reaches its former value. Some cereal pollen grains are present during the clearances, so one must conclude that the forest was removed for their cultivation together, perhaps, with the herding of animals.

It must be remembered that the exposed upland areas were already without trees (as is shown by the peat profile) and could have been used for grazing. The 'slash and burn', cultivate and abandon, type of

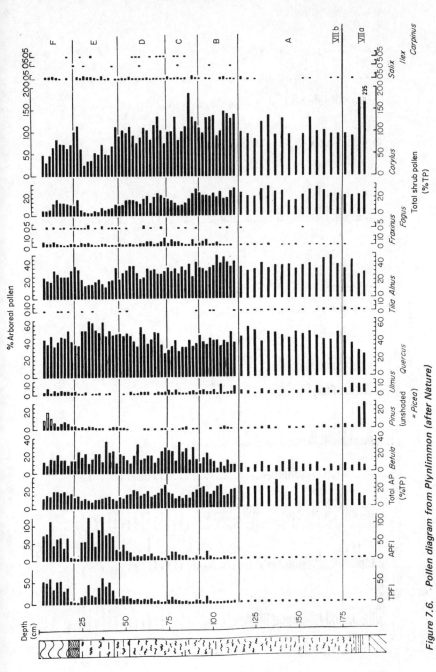

Figure 7.6. Pollen diagram from Plynlimmon (after Nature)

175

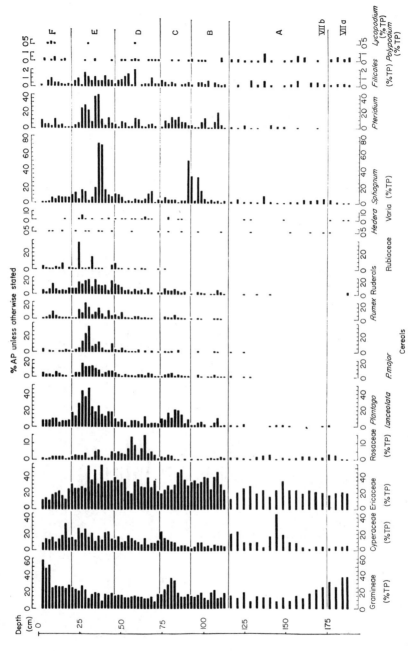

Figure 7.7. Pollen diagram from Plynlimmon

176

economy practised during this period could belong to Bronze Age culture.

Zone C

It is during this zone that the first profound changes in the forest cover and composition occur. This is reflected by prolonged decreases in the arboreal pollen curve and that of the shrubs. Both of these recover by the end of the zone, but do not attain their former levels. Thus one might conclude that irreparable damage has been done to the woodlands during this phase.

Progressive, intermittent forest clearance also leaves its mark on the overall composition of the woodlands, some species suffering and other profiting from these processes. *Fraxinus* (ash) can be seen to increase in its proportional representation in a stepwise manner through periods A, B and C. Following each clearance period ash becomes a more important member of the forest community, taking advantage of the opening up of the woodland canopy. Birch behaves in a rather similar manner, but reaches its peak levels rather before that of ash, reflecting its temporal position in successional sequences. The seeds of birch require light for germination, hence this tree occupies a pioneer position in the succession.

Meanwhile, trees which are either sensitive to clearance, or perhaps are selectively felled, gradually fall in their representation. This process has already been referred to in elm, and is also shown in *Tilia* (lime). This is another tree which may have been of particular interest or value to man[26]. Oak and alder decline during zone C and since alder is rather more abundant in the valleys and at stream sides, their identical behaviour leads one to suppose that the clearances which occurred were not limited to valleys or to hill tops but involved both.

Grass pollen is particularly frequent in this zone, as is that of *Plantago lanceolata*. Turner[27] has suggested that *P. lanceolata* is an indicator of pastoral economy whereas *P. major* and various other ruderals are more frequently associated with an arable one. The ratio of pastoral to arable economy in zone C would seem to be strongly in favour of the former, a conclusion supported by the relative paucity of cereal pollen.

The widespread woodland clearance and pastoral agriculture of zone C may have been due to the activities of Iron Age and Roman peoples.

Zone D

The recovery in trees and shrubs which begins this zone reverts to a gradual forest deterioration which accelerates towards the end of the zone. The indicators of clearance behave in a reciprocal manner, with the exception of the Rosaceae, most of which is of the *Potentilla* type

177

of pollen. This is high during the zone, a feature which is likely to be of local rather than regional significance since most of the species grouped under 'Potentilla type' are insect pollinated and do not produce profuse quantities of airborne pollen. The stratigraphy is still *Eriphorum* peat and the most likely supply of this pollen would be from *Potentilla erecta*. This is a plant which is most frequent in closely grazed turf, being a prostrate species, and its abundance in this zone may indicate that grazing was occurring on the site of the mire.

Zone D is probably to be equated with the post-Roman 'dark ages', and possibly the early 'monastic' period with its associated sheep grazing activities.

Zone E

This is a complex zone in which many changes occur in the pollen spectrum. During it both tree and shrub pollen frequencies fall to their lowest levels, a change which appears to affect alder to a far greater extent than oak. On the argument outlined above, that alder is more abundant in the valleys than on the hills, this could indicate that it is the low lying areas which are suffering most from woodland clearance. The period also shows two major peaks in weed pollen, the second being much larger than the first and accompanied by very high values of cereal pollen.

Evidently it is in this zone that human interference with the vegetation of mid-Wales reaches its greatest extent and involves both pastoral and arable activities, especially in the lowlands and valleys. It is thought that the period corresponds to the enclosures of the Middle Ages, building up to a maximum during the Napoleonic wars when high food prices caused much marginal land to be brought under the plough.

Zone F

The final phase of Zone E, together with Zone F shows a reversal of all these trends. Tree and shrub pollen increase once again and there is a recovery of alder. It is interesting to note the fall in oak at this point, which is probably not a reflection of falling abundance of oak, but simply its changing proportion especially with respect to alder. Increasing pine and spruce *(Picea)* pollen in Zone F is noticeable, as are the falling levels of weed pollen.

The zone covers the last century of history in which mid-Wales has seen a reduction in arable agriculture, depopulation and the expansion of forestry.

The changes documented in Figures 7.6 and 7.7 are due to local variations in land use patterns, therefore neither the conclusion deduced from then nor the zonation system used to analyse them can be applied to areas other than that from which these data originated.

Indeed Turner[28] has shown that changes in pollen profiles may vary in cores from different areas of a single mire, depending upon the land use patterns of the surrounding area.

Nevertheless it is hoped that this case study of mid-Wales involving two pollen profiles has served to illustrate some of the principles and problems of interpretation of such microfossil data. It may also underline the way in which such analyses of microfossils can be integrated with macrofossil stratigraphic studies to produce a more complete picture of the developmental history of a mire. In addition, the regional vegetational change documented by pollen assemblages can serve a useful purpose as chronological markers in the peat profile — a dating technique more rapid, simple and less expensive than radiocarbon dating. Indeed, in a situation where root penetration is abundant, as in the case of the Plynlimmon profile, it may be the only effective way of dating peat initiation.

Microfossil study, then, is a valuable aid to the study of temporal vegetational changes in mires, but has ecological applications and implications which extend far beyond the limits of the peatland ecosystem.

REFERENCES

1. HESLOP-HARRISON, J. 'Pollen wall development.' *Science,* **161,** 230 (1968).
2. BROOKS, J. and SHAW, G. 'Identity of sporopollenin with older kerogen and new evidence for the possible biological source of chemicals in sedimentary rocks.' *Nature, Lond.* **220,** 678 (1968).
3. DIMBLEBY, G.W. 'Soil pollen analysis.' *J. Soil. Sci.* **12,** 1 (1961).
4. IVERSEN, J. 'Retrogressive vegetational succession in the post-glacial.' *J. Ecol.* **52** *(Jubilee Symp. Suppl.)* **52,** (1964).
5. ECHLIN, P. 'Pollen.' *Scientific American.* **218** (4). 80 (1968).
6. FAEGRI, K. and IVERSEN, J. *Textbook of Pollen Analysis.* Oxford (1964).
7. ERDTMAN, G. 'The acetolysis method.' *Svensk. bot. Tidskr.* **54,** 561 (1960).
8. TURNER, J. 'A contribution to the history of forest clearance.' *Proc. R. Soc.* B. **161,** 343 (1965).
9. TAUBER, H. 'Differential pollen dispersion and the interpretation of pollen diagrams.' *Danm. geol. Unders.* (II) **89,** 1 (1965).
10. LIGHTI-FEDEROVICH, S. and RITCHIE, J.C. 'Recent pollen assemblages from the western interior of Canada.' *Rev. palaeobotan. Palynol.* **7,** 297 (1968).
11. SNAYDON, R.W. and BRADSHAW, A.D. 'Differential response to calcium within *Festuca ovina.'* *New Phytol.* **60,** 219 (1961).
12. OLDFIELD, F. 'Problems of mid-post-glacial pollen zonation in part of north-west England.' *J. Ecol.* **53,** 247 (1965).
13. GREEN, B.H. 'Factors influencing the spatial and temporal distribution of *Sphagnum imbricatum.* Hornsch. ex Russ, in the British Isles. *J. Ecol.* **56,** 47 (1968).
14. GODWIN, H. *The History of the British Flora.* C.U.P., Cambridge (1956).
15. PENNINGTON, W. *The History of British Vegetation.* E.U.P., London (1969).

16. MOORE, P.D. and CHATER, E.H. 'Studies in the vegetational history of mid-Wales. I. The post-glacial period in Cardiganshire.' *New Phytol.* **68**, 183 (1969).
17. MOORE, P.D. 'Human influence upon vegetational history in North Cardiganshire.' *Nature, Lond.* **217**, 1006 (1968).
18. MOORE, P.D. and CHATER, E.H. 'The changing vegetation of west-central Wales in the light of human history.' *J. Ecol.* **57**, 361 (1969).
19. MOORE, P.D. 'Studies in the vegetational history of mid-Wales. II. The late-glacial period in Cardiganshire.' *New Phytol.* **69**, 363 (1960).
20. TROELS-SMITH, J. 'Ivy, mistletoe and elm. Climatic indicators — fodder plants.' *Danm. geol. Unders.* **4** (1960).
21. SMITH, A.G. 'The Atlantic-Sub-Boreal transition.' *Proc. Linn. Soc. Lond.* **172**, 38 (1961).
22. GODWIN, H. and WILLIS, E.H. 'Radiocarbon dating of the late-glacial period in Britain.' *Proc. R. Soc.* **B 150**, 199 (1959).
23. GODWIN, H. 'Radiocarbon dating and quaternary research in Britain.' *Proc. R. Soc.* **B 153**, 287 (1960).
24. OLSSON, I.U. (Ed.). *Radiocarbon variations and absolute chronology.* Nobel Symposium 12 (1970).
25. RENFREW, C. 'Carbon 14 and the prehistory of Europe.' *Scientific American.* **225** (4), 63 (1971).
26. TURNER, J. 'The *Tilia* decline: an anthropogenic interpretation.' *New Phytol.* **61**, 328 (1962).
27. TURNER, J. 'The anthropogenic factor in vegetational history. I. Tregaron and Whixall Mosses.' *New Phytol.* **63**, 73 (1964).
28. TURNER, J. 'Post-Neolithic disturbance of British vegetation.' In *Studies in the Vegetational History of the British Isles.* Ed. WALKER, D. and WEST, R.G. C.U.P., Cambridge, 97 (1970).

Chapter Eight

The World Picture

'Anywhere in the world in which water collects on its way down from the catchment to the sea constitutes a template for peat formation'. The process of organic evolution has responded to the potential and the limitations of the mire template and peat producing ecosystems are found throughout the world, (see Katz[2]). However, our knowledge of the mires of the world is limited and much more basic survey is needed before any but the broadest generalisations can be substantiated. The bulk of our knowledge stems from the peat schools of Fennoscandia, Russia, Europe, Britain and North America and our regional knowledge of mires decreases, passing down the list and away from these centres of activity. In this field, references 1-14 are of particular importance.

It may be safely stated that, to date, little or no evidence has come to light which conflicts with the broad generalisations made in Chapters 2 and 3. In fact the most remarkable thing is the overall similarity of the main mire phenomena throughout the world, especially the morphology of the types of mire complex.

As might be expected the greatest inter and intraregional diversity is found in the floristic makeup of the mire vegetation, but even here there are some remarkable similarities.

For example when comparing the vegetation of ombrotrophic mires in a restricted area of the Hudson Bay Lowlands of Canada with those of Fennoscandia Sjörs[10] states: 'The total number of vascular species is 34 in the ombrotrophic mires of the Attawapiskat area and only 23 in the mires of the much larger and more variable N. Fennoscandian area. The latter figure illustrates the well known relative poverty of the N. European flora. Not counting vicarious taxa 15 species are common to the ombrotrophic mires of the two areas. The percentage of common vascular species is 44 for Attawapiskat and no less than 65 for Fennoscandia'.

The similarity in the cryptogamic bottom layer is much greater. For the Bryophytes of the ombrotrophic mires in the two areas, the quotient of similarity (Sorensen[16]) is more than 90%.

Katz recognises more than 140 'bog provinces' each related to a main phytogeographical region and shows again, as might be expected,

181

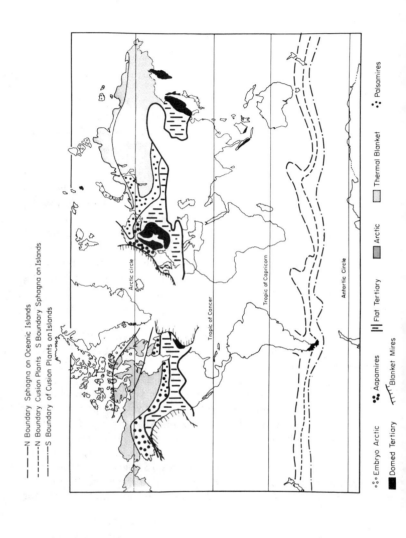

Figure 8.1. Map showing the distribution of the main types of mire complex on a world scale. Primary mires are found throughout the world.

the major differences between the mires of the northern and southern hemispheres and between those of the tropics and the subarctic regions. However both the ombrotrophic and transition mires of the Tierra del Fuego include such species as *Sphagnum magellanicum* and *S. fimbriatum* which are common throughout the northern boreal mires as main peat formers.

The most striking floristic differences are found in the ombrotrophic and transition mires of the Peruvian Uplands. Tasmania and New Zealand, Pidgeon[17] and Davis[18] where the role of Sphagnum as a peat former is taken over by cushion plants, members of the Restionaceae, a family of flowering plants which occurs only in the southern hemisphere. Figure 8.1 attempts to summarise the mire phenomena of the world, using as a basis the mire complex types described above for Europe and Canada with some minor addition. The map is in reality an updating of that given in Bulow[1] and a simplication of those given in Katz[2].

It is emphasised that the boundaries are very approximate and the zonation refers only to lowland mires.

REFERENCES

GENERAL

1. BULOW, K. 'Allgemeine Moorgeologie.' *Hanbuch der Moorkunde,* Bd 1. Berlin (1929).
2. KATZ, N.Y. *Swamps of the World* (In Russian) Nauka Moscow, 257 (1971).

RUSSIA & WESTERN EUROPE

3. OSVALD, H. *Die Hochmoortypen Europas, Festschrift C. Schröter.* Veröff Geobot. Inst. Rübel Zurich, H3 (1925)
4. KATZ, N.Y. *Types of bogs of the U.S.S.R. and Western Europe* (In Russian) Ogiz Moskow (1948).
5. KULCZYNSKI, S. 'Peat Bogs of Polesie.' *Mem. Acad. Sci. Cracovie. Ser. B:* 1-356 (1948).
6. RUUHIJÄRVI, R. 'Uber die regionale Einteilung der Nordfinnischen Moore.' *Ann. Bot. Sco. Vanamo,* **31**, N1 (1960).
7. OSVALD, H. 'Nordamerikanska Mosstyper.' *Svensk. Bot. Tidskr.* **22** N1-2 (1928).
8. DACHNOWSKI-STOKES, A.P. 'Peat deposits of the U.S.A.' *Handbuch der Moorkunde,* **7**. 1-140 Berlin (1933).
9. RIGG, G. The development of Sphagnum bogs in North America. *Bot. Rev.,* **17** N.Z. (1951).
10. SJÖRS, H. 'Bogs and fens on Attawapiskat river.' *Bull. Nat. Mus. Canada.* **186** (1963).
11. HEINSELMAN, M. 'Forest sites, processes in the glacial lake Agassiz region, Minnesota. *Ecol. Monog.* **33** N. 4 (1963).

SOUTH AMERICA

12. AUER, V. 'Die Moore Süd Amerikas, insbesonder Feverlands.' *Handbuch der Moorkunde,* **7.** Berlin (1933).
13. ROIVANEN, H. 'Studien uber die Moore Feverlands.' *Ann. Bot. Soc. Vanamo,* **28,** N2 (1954).

NEW ZEALAND

14. RIGG, H. 'The Pakihi Bogs of Westport New Zealand.' *Trans. Roy. Soc. NZ Bot,* 1N7 (1962).

15. ANDERSON, J. 'The flora of the peat swamp forests of Sarawak and Brunei.' *Gardens Bull., Singapore,* **20,** pt. 2 (1973).

16. SORENSEN, Th. 'A method of establishing groups of equal amplitude in plant sociology based on species content.' *K. Danske Vidensk. Selsk. Biol. Skr.* **5,** No. 4, 1-34 (1948).
17. PIDGEON, I.M. 'The ecology of the central, coastal area of New South Wales.' *Proc. Linn. Soc. N.S. Wales,* **63,** pt. 1-2 (19)
18. DAVIS, C. 'Preliminary survey of the vegetation near New Harbour, South West Tasmania.' *Proc. Roy. Soc. Tasmania.*

Chapter Nine

The World's Resource

As man's population grows and his cultural and industrial development continues at an accelerating pace, so his demands upon the natural resources of the planet increase yearly. He requires raw materials and energy for industrial and domestic uses and food production must keep pace with his expanding population. It is natural that he should turn to all possible sources to supply these needs to ensure his continued survival and advancement. When his various demands conflict with one another he seeks compromise solutions, and thus his search for raw materials may despoil land needed for agriculture. Similarly his demands for energy take him to a variety of sources, many of which lead to serious problems of chemical and thermal pollution. Nevertheless, higher standards of living are demanded by every man and this involves higher consumption of energy per capita of the world's population.

Long before the exploitation of the conventional 'fossil fuels' (coal and oil), wood was used as an energy source, together with water in western areas of Britain in connection with the wool industry[1]. Where the resource was available, peat has also been a valuable source of power, though ·it is unlikely that it could have supplied the energy necessary for the industrial revolution in Europe. However, in modern times peat is still used, sometimes on an industrial scale, as an energy resource, particularly in those countries where peat is abundant and easily extracted.

The use of peat in agriculture and horticulture has led to a renewed demand for the commodity even in countries which are not rich in peat deposits. Thus the value of peat as an economic resource is becoming increasingly recognised.

In this chapter we shall first look at the world distribution of this resource and then at its uses in various industries.

WORLD DISTRIBUTION OF THE RESOURCE

As we have seen, peatlands are most typical of the boreal and arctic regions of the northern hemisphere, but they are by no means confined to these areas[2]. Temperate latitudes of both northern and southern hemispheres have peat deposits, though they are far commoner in the north. Tasmania has small peat deposits of *Sphagnum* together with species of *Restio* and *Malalenca* and some of these mires are exploited commercially even at altitudes of 2 500 ft in forest country. Australia is not rich in exploitable peat deposits, but a large bog of two square miles in extent and up to 25 ft deep has been found near Canberra and is to be exploited for horticulture. It is estimated that the 30×10^6 cubic yards of peat found in this single bog will supply the horticultural needs of Australia for the next 50 years.

New Zealand has larger deposits of peat and it is estimated that there are 643 square miles of peatlands, mainly on the North Island. This comprises 0.6% of the total area of the islands.

Tropical and subtropical peat deposits are probably far more extensive than is realised. In South America, Uruguay and Paraguay possess considerable areas of peatland dominated by *Taxodium* and *Eucalyptus* tree genera. Pakistan has local peat deposits, mainly in river deltas; reserves are estimated at 200 million tons of dry peat. Mangrove swamps are important peat producing communities in Africa and in Florida. Cuba and Guyana, Malaya and Indonesia also have extensive peatlands which are often cultivated for the growing of such crops as sugarcane. Such agricultural use of peatlands is also practised in Israel where about 5 000 hectares of peat formed mainly from *Cyperus* and *Polygonum* are under cultivation in the northern part of the country. Rice is grown on 70 000 hectares of peatland in Japan, which constitutes about a third of the country's total of peatlands.

As can be seen from Table 9.1, Europe contains a significant quantity of peatlands, especially the countries of northern Europe, Finland, East and West Germany, United Kingdom, Ireland, Sweden and Poland. Of these, Finland has the greatest resource. It is estimated that there are almost ten million hectares of peatland in Finland, almost a third of the total area of the country. This represents about 100 million cubic metres of peat. In Germany there are one and a half million hectares of peatland, two thirds of which are found in West Germany. This figure is roughly the same as that for the United Kingdom, a breakdown of which is given in Table 9.2.

Sweden has a similar area of peatlands, about 1½ million hectares, but in this case it represents 14.5% of the total area of the country, whereas for the United Kingdom it is only 6.6%. Poland also has a peatland area amounting to 5% of its total land surface, much of which is given over to agriculture and forestry. Other European countries contain smaller peat reserves, fragmented by industrial and agricultural development.

TABLE 9.1
THE WORLD'S PEAT RESOURCES (HECTARES)

Canada	129 500 000
U.S.S.R. *	71 500 000
Finland	10 000 000
U.S.A.	7 500 000
Norway	3 000 000
United Kingdom	1 582 000
Sweden	1 500 000
Poland	1 500 000
West Germany	1 129 000
Iceland	1 000 000
Indonesia	700 000
East Germany	489 000
Cuba	200 000
Japan	200 000
Eire *	172 000
New Zealand	166 000
Hungary	100 000
Netherlands	100 000
Denmark	60 000
France	60 000
Italy	60 000
Czechoslovakia	33 000
Austria	22 000
Romania	6 000
Israel	5 000
Others	400 000
Total	230 484 000

* These are exploitable reserves and therefore
underestimate total peatland area.

TABLE 9.2
AREA OF PEATLAND IN THE UNITED KINGDOM
(AFTER ROBERTSON AND JOWSEY[3])

Country	Peatland Area	Land Surface (%)
Scotland	821 381	10·7
England	361 690	2·8
Northern Ireland	240 000	17·8
Wales	158 770	7·5
	1 581 841	6·6

In Iceland, hand cut peat has been the most important source of fuel until recent times. Now there is an emphasis upon mire reclamation and drainage. In the United States, peat resources are mainly concentrated in the northern region and along the Atlantic coast, south to Florida.

The greatest areas of peatlands to be found in the world are in the two countries Canada and the Soviet Union. Almost certainly the latter contains greater areas of peat than the former and the figures in Table 9.1 are misleading because of the differing purposes for which they were produced. The Canadian figure of almost thirty million hectares (500 000 square miles) comes from N.W. Radforth in his opening address to the International Peat Society in 1968. It is a rough estimate of the total extent of 'muskeg' in the country. The Russian figure is a precise one based upon a survey of exploitable deposits. The two figures are therefore not strictly comparable and the Russian claim to ownership of over sixty percent of the world's peat resources remains unchallenged. We do not have a precise figure of exploitable deposits in Canada, apart from the 110 000 hectares of surveyed mires. This is obviously a gross underestimate of Canada's peat resources. Between them, Canada and the Soviet Union probably contain well over 80% of the world's peat resources.

PEAT EXPLOITATION

The quantity of peat present in any country does not necessarily bear any relationship to the degree of exploitation to which that peat is submitted. Table 9.3 gives a breakdown in percentage terms of the

TABLE 9.3
PEAT EXPLOITATION (AFTER SHERIDAN[14])

U.S.S.R.	95·70
Eire	2·04
West Germany	0·85
U.S.A.	0·29
East Germany	0·27
Netherlands	0·21
Sweden	0·16
Canada	0·13
Norway	0·08
South Korea	0·06
Poland	0·05
Others	0·16

Figures are percentages of annual world harvest of peat

188

world's peat exploitation. It can be seen that the Soviet Union dominates the world exploitation of peat, the bulk of the harvested peat being used internally as an energy source. Canada, on the other hand, exploits little of its peatlands and exports 90% of the produce to the U.S.A. for horticulture.

Eire is the only country apart from Russia which uses peat as an energy resource. It also exports large quantities to the United Kingdom for horticulture.

It is natural that many of the great improvements in peat harvesting techniques have originated in Russia, where large scale peat exploitation dates back to the early 18th century. In the middle of the 19th century attempts were made to use peat as an industrial fuel source for textile mills and by 1914 Russia had the first electric power station in the world which operated on peat fuel. At the turn of this century Russia was harvesting 1.65 million tons of peat per annum.

Since the Revolution, further emphasis has been placed upon peat exploitation and harvesting methods. The early excavating techniques were replaced by hydraulic and dredging methods, but in 1928 a new system termed 'milling' was introduced. This method now accounts for 90% of the peat harvested in the Soviet Union and for the bulk of that harvested in Eire and in Canada.

The milling method consists of scratching the surface inch of the peat deposit, disturbing and turning it by rotating drums fitted with wire pins. This disturbed, aerated peat is then allowed to dry for two or three days before harvesting when the next layer of peat can be milled. The harvesting of the loose, dried layer is effected by vacuum operated machines which suck up the fragmented peat. In Russia combine machines with an annual production capacity of 30 000—35 000 tons per harvesting season are about to enter service. Total annual production is 80 million tons of peat.

A limitation in the application of this technique is the extent of wood in the peat deposit. When the wood content becomes high, this type of harvesting is not efficient. Tree stumps are particularly hazardous and have to be removed before milling can take place. Grading machines can also be used for the removal of wood from milled peat.

Poorly humified *Sphagnum* peat produces a distinctive type of milled peat which is termed 'litter' in North America and 'moss peat' in Eire. This is of especial use as a soil conditioner in horticulture or can be compressed into boards with a high insulating capacity. Other types of milled peat may also be compressed into briquettes after drying to a moisture content of 10% (moisture content on harvesting is about 55%).

The extraction of 'sod peat' from vertical faces by machines is still of importance in Eire and in the Soviet Union. It is spread to dry on the mire surface and then stacked. Hydraulic methods of extraction are still used in parts of Canada where water and climatic conditions are favourable. High pressure water is used to cut and erode peat from exposed faces.

In Russia and Canada especially, the transportation of peat is a considerable problem since peatlands are often remote from the industrial areas. It is probably this remoteness which has delayed the exploitation of Canada's great resources. In Russia narrow gauge railways are used for transportation of the milled peat in hoppers.

THE USES OF PEAT

Since peat consists largely of undecomposed vegetable material, it is of a high energy content. Its physical structure is often fibrous and spongy, which gives it a high water holding capacity. Also, its chemical structure is such that it has great powers of cation retention. These three major properties have resulted in man's use of peat in various technological processes, largely power production, agricultural and the chemical industries. We shall now look at some of the applications of these properties in industry and agriculture.

Peat as an Energy Resource

The energy content of peat, expressed as its calorific value, varies between different peat types. The utilisation of this energy resource in Europe mainly as a domestic fuel is of considerable antiquity. As we saw in an earlier section, the Soviet Union has exploited its peat deposits by driving a total of seventy power stations mainly on milled peat. Some of these stations have a capacity of over 300 MW, and between them they consume 70% of the peat harvested in the U.S.S.R. The only other country which uses the energy of peat to produce electricity is the Republic of Ireland which has a total of eight peat fired power stations with a combined capacity of 387.5 MW. Approximately two million tons of peat are consumed annually in these stations, three quarters of which is milled peat.

For some time efforts have been made to convert peat into a coke material for use in smelting and blast furnaces. Russia now claims to have developed a process which is able to produce 'coke' and 'semicoke' from milled peat and operates blast furnaces with the product.

The use of peat as a domestic fuel is declining, but still persists in remoter areas of Ireland, Scotland, West Germany, Finland and Russia.

Horticultural and Agricultural Uses of Peat

In all countries apart from Russia and Eire, the major use of peat is in agricultural and horticultural fields. Here its value is dependent upon a variety of properties,

1. Its organic content and high energy capacity makes peat a valuable metabolic substrate for soil microflora, hence serving the purpose of an organic manure
2. The fibrous nature of peat and its resulting waterholding capacity assists water retention in soils and improves their structure
3. The high base exchange capacity of peat, derived especially from the polyuronic acids in *Sphagnum* cell walls, makes the commodity valuable for the retention of cations in the soil, particularly if it is low in clay content (see Chapter 5)
4. Peat alters the physical properties of soil, especially its thermal properties, because of its very high specific heat. This will affect both the microbes and higher living organisms in the soil.

Because of these various properties of peat and the consequent changes in soil which result from its application, a number of characters are required of horticultural peat which enhance these effects. A list of these characters has been published by workers at Michigan State University in the United States[5]. This includes organic matter content, decomposition, acidity, water content, weedseed contamination and structure.

The organic content of peat is important both as an energy reserve for microflora and as the site of its high base exchange capacity. Peat must therefore be defined according to its organic content for horticultural purposes. The level accepted by the Federal Trade Commission of the United States is 75% organic matter, below which it is illegal to market a commodity labelled 'peat'. Thus in peat exploitation it becomes unprofitable to harvest peats with a high mineral content. These are usually the basal layers of peatlands and it has become a common practice to harvest the organic layers of the upper part of the mire and to use the lower layers for potato growing *in situ*. Obviously the peats formed under more ombrotrophic conditions will contain less inorganic (ash) material than those formed under rheotrophic ones. For example *Sphagnum* moss peat generally contains less than 10% of its dry weight as ash. Hypnoid moss peats formed under rheotrophic conditions may contain up to 20%.

The sponge-like properties of peat make it important as a means of retaining water in free-draining soils. Again, the water holding capacity of a peat depends to a large extent upon the type of peat from which it was formed. Below is a list of the minimum waterholding capacity specified by the United States Federal Government for various peat types. It is expressed as a percentage by weight of the ovendry weight peats[6].

Sphagnum moss peat	800%
Other moss peats	400%
Reedsedge peat	400%
Humus peat	200%

These figures apply to peat samples which have been saturated with water for 18–24 hrs. and then dried at $105°C$ to constant weight.

The water holding capacity of peat is a feature associated with the capillarity of its fibrous structure. It is useful therefore to obtain some measure of its fibrousness. For this purpose a 'fibre' is defined as having a minimum length of 0.15 mm and a grading system has been constructed by the American Society for Testing and Materials based on the percentage fibre content of a peat, where

$$\text{percentage fibre content} = \frac{\text{dry weight of fibres} > 0.15 \text{ mm} \times 100}{\text{total dry weight}}$$

Cameron[6], working in Pennsylvania, has found that *Sphagnum* peats tend to have fibre contents of over 66%, reed sedge peats 33–66% and humus peats less than 33%. However this measure is probably more closely related to the degree of humification than the nature of the peatforming vegetation. Fibre content is inversely related to density, which may be of importance where peat is sold on a volume basis.

Horticulture and agriculture probably represent the most important world use of peat. In the United Kingdom 90% of its annual peat harvest finds its way onto the horticultural market, a total of 160 000 tons, in addition to which it imports a further 60 000 tons mainly from the Irish Republic each year. In 1966 the United States harvested 611 085 tons and imported a further 293 843 tons, the bulk of which was used in horticulture. This represents a total of $18 million worth of peat, which makes peat exploitation a profitable venture in North America.

To be of greatest value in increasing plant productivity, the peat may be combined with ammonia and mineral nutrients, the latter becoming bound by the exchange properties of the peat. These bound cations are released gradually into the soil by exchange with other ions or on the decomposition of the organic matter. In the Soviet Union 100 million tons of peat are harvested annually and much of this is treated with ammonia and minerals. Two methods are used; the first involves treatment of the peat before harvesting by spraying on the nutrients.

The surface peat is then milled and collected pneumatically. In a second process the nutrient solution is introduced into peat after harvesting. The peat is then dried and transported.

A fairly recent development in the horticultural industry is the use of fibre pots made of compressed peat. These serve the various functions listed above together with facilitating transplantation of young plants by avoiding root disturbance. Roots can penetrate the pots and the latter eventually decompose into the soil. Norway has led the world for many years in the production of these peat pots. In 1967 400 million were produced in Norway and a further 50 million in Finland. Other countries involved in the pot making industry include Denmark, Ireland, Czechoslovakia, Poland and Japan.

Insulation

During the 1930s, Russia began to exploit the high thermal insulation properties of certain peats, particularly poorly decomposed *Sphagnum* peats. They compressed such peats into boards with very low thermal conductivity coefficients (less than 0.55 kcal) coupled with low density ($170-220$ kg/m^3). Currently $100\ 000$ m^3 of such boards are produced annually and these have proved particularly valuable in the poultry industry where they are used for housing stock.

A similar application of the thermal properties has been made in Norway where compressed bales of peat are used in the foundations of railways built on soils subject to frost heaving. The insulating properties of the peat prevent damage to railway lines by this process.

Chemical Uses of Peat

Poorly humified *Sphagnum* peat is rich in carbohydrates which are easily hydrolysed — yields of monosaccharide of 45–55% dry weight have been obtained on hydrolysis. Despite this, peat is not easily digested and assimilated by animals and is of no value as a stock feed, mainly because the easily hydrolysed polyose carbohydrates are enclosed within tough sheaths. However, liberation of these low molecular weight polymers provides a useful growth medium for yeasts which can then be used for fodder. This process is used in the Soviet Union for the production of ethyl alcohol, together with furfural, polyhydric alcohols, hydroxy acids, etc., dilute sulphuric acid being used as a hydrolysing agent. More recently a process whereby atomised concentrated sulphuric acid is sprayed onto air dried peat has been developed; this results in the hydrolysis of much of the longer chain polysaccharide component and therefore proves a more efficient use of the material.

Other chemical constituents of peats which are used in industry are waxes, bitumens, resins and oils. These are used in the USSR in many industries, including machine building, plastics, leather, varnish and dyes.

THE CULTIVATION OF PEATLANDS

The most acute problem involved in the cultivation of peatlands is the control of water table, since the majority of domesticated plants require a soil water regime which does not involve waterlogging. Thus drainage is usually necessary, but the extent of the drainage will vary with the crop to be raised. An exception to this general rule is the North American annual grass *Zizania aquatica* (wild rice) which was used as a food plant by prehistoric cultures. Considerable efforts are now being made to exploit the wetlands of Canada by the growing of wild rice which does not necessitate any drainage. Similarly, vast areas of peatland in Japan are used for the cultivation of rice *(Oryza sativa)*.

On a world scale, the most important type of agriculture associated with peatlands is forestry. Since the majority of commercial tree species do not grow well in waterlogged environments, drainage of some type is usually necessary, even if it involves only a ploughing of the surface peat into ridges and furrows. Some work has been done in Czechoslovakia[8] upon the optimal depth of water table for growing various conifer species, and the results were as shown in Table 9.4.

TABLE 9.4
OPTIMAL DEPTH OF WATER TABLE

Species	1st year's growth	2nd year's growth
Pinus sylvestris	60 cm	60–80 cm
Picea excelsa	40 cm	60 cm
Pinus strobus	60 cm	60–80 cm

A water table which was closer than 20 cm to the peat surface led to complete growth stagnation and similarly a water table deeper than a metre led to severe deterioration in growth. Thus the degree of drainage necessary for optimal growth is quite critical and it is liable to be different for differing climatic regimes. Thus in drier climates a higher water table may prove advantageous, whereas in regions of high atmospheric humidity the reverse may be true.

The means of effecting the correct degree of drainage will depend upon the physical properties of the particular peat type, since the degree to which lateral seepage of water occurs in peat varies

194

considerably. For example, in Ireland on domed mire peats it has been found that ditches of 1m in depth have little effect upon the water table at distances greater than 1.8m from the ditch edge[9]. On the other hand, a sedge bog (*Scirpus caespitosus*) in Newfoundland, appreciable lowering of water tables was observed 11m from such ditches[10].

The final water table is likely to be affected further by the precise crop grown, for example, O'Hare[11] in Ireland has compared water tables in peat beneath Sitka spruce *(Picea sitchensis)* and an adjacent grass sward. He found that the water table beneath the trees was 40 cm lower than that under grass. Haikurainen[12] has suggested that such differences in water regime beneath trees on peat is largely due to the interception of rainfall by the forest canopy and its subsequent evaporation rather than the higher transpiration rates in forest. Rutter and Fourt[13] have demonstrated that evaporation rates from forest are indeed appreciably greater than those from grassland by a factor of about two, the differential being greatest in months of water deficit.

Final water tables after reclamation are therefore dependent upon:
1. Physical properties of the peat
2. Depth and distance apart of drainage ditches
3. The overall climate
4. The crop grown on the reclaimed peat.

In addition to the problem of water levels, the levels of plant nutrients in reclaimed peat may also be limiting. Thus the majority of peats need to be fertilised with certain minerals, particularly phosphorus, potassium and nitrogen before good crop yields are obtained.

For example a grass crop grown on cut-over domed mire peat in Ireland required 275 lb N, 37 lb P and 188 lb K per acre for a good crop[14]. However, the crop represented recovery rates of these nutrients at 80%, 78% and 83% of the application respectively. Thus although fertilisation is necessary for peatland cultivation, it affords an efficient medium for the retention and recycling of the nutrients supplied.

The need to supply nitrate to crops in reclaimed peat is due to the impaired natural nitrogen cycle on these soils. In virgin acid peatlands there is virtually no nitrification, i.e. conversion of ammonia to nitrate, due to the absence of the necessary bacteria[15]. When such peats are reclaimed it may take several years of liming and cultivation before these organisms are able to invade and recycle the nitrogen present in the peat. Meanwhile nitrates must be supplied to the crops grown.

In addition to forestry and pastureland, reclaimed peatlands have become highly valued for growing vegetables and for horticulture. In Russia potatoes and onions are frequent crops. In the Netherlands and East Anglia bulbs are an important industry on reclaimed peat. In

Michigan, U.S.A., peatlands are used for growing Kentucky blue grass *(Poa pratensis)* for lawns; seed germinating on peat takes about 8–16 months to form a dense sward, when it can be cut into strips and rolled up for transportation.

SECONDARY PRODUCERS IN PEATLANDS

In the preceding section we have been considering the modification and harvesting of wetlands mainly in terms of primary production, i.e. the harvesting of plant crops. An exception was afforded by the use of reclaimed peatland for grassland, where a secondary producer, cow or sheep, would be harvested. However, in the United States there has been some considerable attempt to harvest the secondary production of natural wetlands, mainly through waterfowl management.

Waterfowl hunting has long been a popular sport in the United States, but scientific control measures have become necessary to maintain a sensible cropping rate. For example in 1960 approximately 9.8 million ducks were bagged in the U.S.A., largely mallard, green winged teal and American widgeon[16]. In 1964 the kill was increasing in some areas by 123% per annum. However, by limiting the numbers of each species which may be cropped it is now felt that the population levels are stable and that hunting is responsible for only a very small proportion of the total deaths among wildfowl, possibly as low as 4%. The estimation of the permissible crop is based upon careful surveys of population levels at various times of the year.

Meanwhile efforts are made to create and maintain wetland habitats suitable for waterfowl, both by creating artificial ponds and by retarding hydroseral successions. The latter is achieved by periodic draining of ponds and breaking up the exposed mud. They are then left dry for one year, allowing a degree of decomposition to occur after which reflooding takes place. It is found that this also assists in nutrient release and recycling.

Thus peat and peatlands have been exploited for a variety of purposes in different countries. In some countries the reclamation of peatlands for agriculture and forestry is of vital importance, such as in Finland where a third of the country is peat covered and already a million hectares have been reclaimed. In Canada also peatland reclamation for forestry and agriculture is likely to become increasingly important in the near future. In the European Low Countries and the British 'fenlands' such reclamation has been proceeding for hundreds of years until wetland habitats have become fragmented and a cause of considerable concern to conservationists. The problems involved in peatland conservation will form the theme of our final chapter.

196

REFERENCES

1. TREVELYAN, G.M. *English Social History,* Longmans, New York (1942).
2. TIBBETS, T.E. 'Peat resources of the world — a review.' *Proc. 3rd Int. Peat Congress,* Quebec, 8 (1968).
3. ROBERTSON, R.A. and JOWSEY, P.C. 'Peat resources and development in the United Kingdom.' *Proc. 3rd Int. Peat Congress,* Quebec. 13 (1968).
4. SHERIDAN, E.T. Peat. Minerals Yearbook, U.S. Dept. of the Interior (1965).
5. LUCAS, R.E., RIEKE, P.E., and FARNHAM, R.S. Peats for soil improvement and soil mixes.' *Michigan State Univ. Coop. Ext. Service, Ext. Bull. no. 516, Farm Sc. Ser.* (1966).
6. CAMERON, C.C. 'Peat deposits of Northeastern Pennsylvania.' *Geol. Survey Bull.* **1317-A,** U.S. Dept. of the Interior (1970).
7. RAKOVSKII, V.E. *et al.* 'The scientific basis of peat chemistry and peat engineering in the USSR.' *Proc. 3rd Int. Peat Congress,* Quebec, 378 (1968).
8. FERDA, J. 'Determination of the optimum height of the groundwater level for young plantations on boggy soil.' *Proc. 3rd Int. Peat Congress,* Quebec, 268 (1968)*.
9. BURKE, W. 'Drainage of blanket peat at Glenamoy.' *Proc. 2nd Int. Peat Congress,* Leningrad, II, 809 (1969).
10. RAYMENT, A.F. and COOPER, D.J. 'Drainage of Newfoundland peat soils for agricultural purposes.' *Proc. 3rd Int. Peat Congress,* Quebec, 345 (1968).
11. O'HARE, P.J. 'A comparison of the effect of young forest and grassland on the water table in blanket peat.' *U.C.W. Symposia in Agric. Meteorol.* No. 13, Aberystwyth (1970).
12. HAIKURAINEN, L. 'On the influence of cutting on the water economy of drained peatlands.' *Acta for. fenn.* **82** (2), 45 (1967).
13. RUTTER, A.J. and FOURT, D.F. 'Studies in the water relations of *Pinus sylvestris* in plantation conditions. 3. A comparison of soil water changes and estimates of total evaporation on four afforested sites and one grass-covered site.' *J. appl. Ecol.* **2,** 197 (1965).
14. COLE, A.J. 'Grass production on cut-over raised bog—nitrogen, phosphorus and potassium requirements.' *Proc. 3rd Int. Peat Congress,* Quebec, 251 (1968).
15. KUSTER, E. and GARDINER, J.J. 'Influence of fertilizers on microbial activities in peatland.' *Proc. 3rd Int. Peat Congress,* Quebec, 314 (1968).
16. OWEN, O.S. *Natural Resource Conservation.* Macmillan (1971).

Chapter Ten

Conservation

'Conservation is taken to mean the sensible utilisation of natural resources'.

THE RESOURCE

The approximate statistics of the worlds peat resource is 230 million hectares covered with 330×10^9 dry tonnes of organic matter, representing $1,700 \times 10^{16}$ kcal. of potential energy, holding 180×10^9 litres of water and, if oxidised, capable of producing 500×10^9 tonnes of carbon dioxide.

The rate of peat formation is at its maximum 3 tonnes per hectare per year. If all the mires of the world were forming peat at this rate it would give a figure for total world production of 450 million tonnes. However, the deposition of peat in most mires is much less than this and in cutaways (that is areas from which the peat has been removed) it is often nil. The contemporary rate of exploitation of approximately 90 million tonnes per annum is thus greater than its rate of replacement. Peat must therefore be considered as a nonrenewable resource and its conservation considered from that standpoint.

The following questions must therefore be answered:
1. Are there any direct, or side effects relating to the removal and use of peat which should be included in the overall equations of the economics of exploitation?
2. Is the full potential of the resource being realised, that is could peat be put to any better use?

THE EFFECTS OF EXPLOITATION

From first principles, it is obvious that the mires of the world play a significant role in the global cycles of water and carbon dioxide, (see Deevey[1]). They must therefore have at least some effect on the 'state' of the biosphere *in toto*. It is however, easy to speculate on the effects of say, 'the combustion of the total peat resource'. 500×10^9 tonnes of carbon dioxide would be released into the atmosphere and could increase the 'greenhouse' effect altering the overall pattern of macroclimate. Such projections can, however, be relegated to the realms of speculative science fiction and resource planning must be based on hard fact.

There is much evidence concerning the importance of peat deposits and intact mire complexes to the ecological balance of the regions in which they are situated, for example, upland peats and runoff control (Conway and Millar[2]) lowland peats and drainage control (Mamak[3]) and of mire complexes of all types controlling the balance of whole catchment systems (Dachnowski-Stokes[4], Kulczynski[5]).

The main hydrological argument revolves around the fact that peat acts as a reservoir, increasing the surface retention (storage capacity) of the landscape. The problem comes in assessing the importance of this increased storage in relation to the other hydrological characteristics, and hence the ecological balance of the catchment. The volume of water held in the mire reservoir serves only one natural function which is the maintenance of an active mire ecosystem. If water is removed from the reservoir peat growth will cease and the reservoir will eventually disappear. The mire can thus only act as a balancing reservoir, smoothing the pattern of outflow during periods of heavy

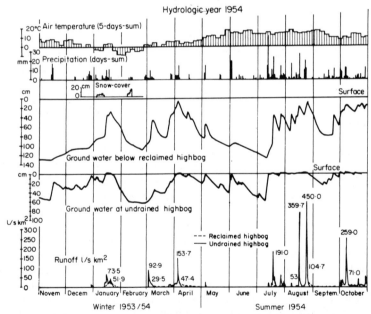

Figure 10.1. The fluctuation of air temperature, rainfall, ground water table and run-off for the hydrological year 1954 with a very wet summer (Redrawn after Baden and Egglesman[6])

199

rainfall, snowmelt and drought. Extensive measurements have been carried out by the German State Peat Research Station near Hamburg, where the water balance of two areas of domed ombrotrophic mire have been compared. One area was of intact mire under vegetation dominated by *Calluna vulgaris,* the second adjacent area had been drained in 1912 with tile drains and was under grass. Figure (modified after Baden and Egglesmann[6]) presents comparative data for the year 1954. It is clear that the drained mire has a much more pronounced effect in controlling the runoff than its undrained (natural) counterpart. The reason is obvious. Once the mire is fully charged with water the reservoir has no further capacity and flash runoff will occur. Any active mire must be fully charged with water for the bulk of the year, thus a partly drained mire should be more effective in controlling flash runoff. However, one fact must be borne in mind. The surface peats of a drained mire are open to oxidative decay and the reservoir is therefore a wasting asset.

All these factors must be taken into account if the 'catchment control' argument is going to be used as a factor when deciding what constitutes the sensible utilisation of any particular area of peatland.

UTILISATION OF PEAT DEPOSITS *IN SITU*

If there is any indication that the removal of a peat deposit may have adverse effects within the landscape unit then it would seem appropriate to utilise the peat deposit *in situ.* Such utilisation will be mainly for forestry, agriculture or horticulture and much research is being carried out which is aimed at maximising the return from such operations.

AGRICULTURAL USE OF RHEOTROPHIC PEATS

The rheotrophic mires offer the greatest potential for direct agricultural use. Their peats are charged with the mineral nutrients eroded from the catchment over long periods of time and once drained they produce first class farmland. The problem is drainage and subsequent wastage of the peat due to oxidative decay. The classic example is the Fenlands of East Anglia (Tansley[7]). These were extensive rheophilous mire complexes which have been subject to drainage and agriculture for well over 500 years. There is much documentary evidence which shows that they have been a long term asset of first class agricultural land. However, in places the contemporary rate of peat wastage is enormous, and continued exploitation is now dependent upon extensive systems from which the water has to be lifted by pumping up to the main dykes which are embanked high above the level of the fields. Where such mires are situated in low lying coastal areas, wastage can bring them below sea level, thus necessitating the construction and maintenance of adequate sea defences (see Prus-Chakinski[8]).

This is a worldwide problem of increasing importance and hence two further examples will be outlined.

The Holland Marsh, Bradford, Ontario, Canada

Holland Marsh is the largest area of much soils (rheotrophic peats) in Ontario. The area is ideally suited to cool weather crops, such as carrots, onions, parsnips, cabbage and lettuce. It is low lying in relation to the lands around it, so soil and air temperatures are usually lower on the mire. High water holding capacity is another mire advantage providing a steady water supply. Other things being equal this assures steady uninterrupted crop growth. Attempts are made to hold the water table about 80 cm below the soil surface (see Walter[9]).

Drainage operations were begun in 1925 and the area first came into production in the 1930s. In 1966 approximately 7500 acres were under cultivation yielding a return on all vegetables of about $5½ million. However, many of the farms situated on the thinnest peats at the edge of the mire are already out of production due to peat wastage.

The Everglades, Florida

The Florida Everglades are shrinking alarmingly owing to the extensive drainage of their component swamplands mainly for truck farming. It has been estimated that the Everglades are subsiding at the rate of 3 cm per annum, and that if this continues, the seepage of salt water into the system will cause a complete change in the character of this unique mire complex destroying much of its wildlife potential and interest.

FORESTRY

The success of silviculture on peat is based on adequate drainage and fertilisation, and hence afforestation faces the same problems of peat wastage and eventual destruction of the peat resource. Added to this is the fact that forestry operations are usually on a massive scale, as is the Finnish programme, for example, where 350 000 hectares are being prepared each year for afforestation. Replacement of living mire systems by forests on such a scale must have marked effects on the climate and water balance (especially the river flow characteristics) of the region. Whether such changes will be detrimental in the long term remains to be seen.

UPLAND PEATS

The uses of upland peats, especially blanket mire complexes, face similar problems. In Britain extensive areas are managed for summer rough pasture and for the rearing of the grouse *(Lagopus).* Management is by drainage and rotational burning, the former to increase the amount of heather (*Calluna vulgaris*) in the vege 10.1 , the latter to ensure an adequate supply of young heather shoots which are the staple diet of the grouse. The combined practice can lead to massive breakdown of the mire ecosystem and the peat blanket is eventually lost. In this way large areas of the British uplands have been turned into wet deserts of little use to man or nature (see Bower[10]).

Thus it would seem that development of the resource potential *in situ,* poses the same problems as removal of the resource, that is loss of the peat reservoir. The end product in both cases is often scrub pasture of wasteland of no direct economic value (see Fritton[11]).

In some cases this is not so, for example where the mire system had developed over-rich alluvial deposits, when removal of the peat will expose terrain which is of great value to long term agricultural use. One of the best examples of this is the area around Flanders Moss in Perthshire in Scotland where removal of part of two great domed ombrotrophic mires has provided some of the best agricultural soils in Scotland. In such cases the combined use of the resource is advocated.

To this end Bord Na Mona (The Irish Peat Board) is undertaking the necessary research to determine the potential of the terrain which is left after partial removal of the peat resource. About ½ million acres of Ireland's total peatlands is ombrotrophic mire, in actual fact a series of domed ombrotrophic mires (Zone 7B, see Page 28). The ombrotrophic peat is useless for direct crop production even if massive and regular fertilisation is undertaken. However, much of the ombrotrophic peats are underlain by rheotrophic and transition peats developed on clay and alluvial deposits. Removal of the bulk of the peat strata, leaving about 150 cm of the basal peat produces, after adequate drainage and fertilisation, productive land of high agricultural value. The potential of these new 'Irish Fenlands' perhaps rivals that of their East Anglian counterparts. The problem is, for how long?, and what will remain after complete peat wastage?

To date the only real long term success story of utilisation of peat deposits *in situ,* is the cranberry and blueberry industries of North America. A whole variety of cranberries and blueberries, *Vaccinium* spp. can be grown directly on ombrotrophic and transition mires. Their cultivation does not require drainage for the simple reason that the original cultivars of the crop plants were members of the natural mire vegetation. This very valuable crop can therefore be grown with minimal effect on the peat deposit. The possibilities and potential of other species such as the cloudberry, *Rubus chamaemorus,* and wild rice, *Zizania aquatica,* are being actively studied. Some species, such as *Rubus chamaemorus, R. arcticus* and *Vaccinium microcaspum* are grown for liquor production in eastern Europe and the Soviet Union.

THE POTENTIAL OF THE PEAT

Peat is the fossilised excess of thousands of years of photosynthesis, it is thus a storehouse of energy and organic chemicals. The two main uses of peat are as fuel and as soil conditioners of various types, see Chapter 9. However sophisticated the process and efficient the caloric recovery (see Ivanov[12]), the current rate of destruction of the world's peat reserves for power production must be regarded as excessive. In a world which is characterised by expanding desert regions and the need for higher levels of agricultural production, the combustion of peat must be regarded, at least in part, as unwise use of the resource. The long term requirements of peat for soil conditioning, especially in the arid zones, must be considered on a world scale and as a world problem.

Recent findings, like those of Tolpa[13] who have reported the presence of chemical compounds which have properties as biostimulators and the development of soilless potting composts which increase not only the value of the peat resource many fold, but the efficiency of its use in agriculture and horticulture (see Atkins[14]) emphasise this fact still further.

As with all resource planning the problem is that we will never have all the pertinent knowledge and therefore it must be accepted that at least some of the potential of the resource will be lost. The work of the International Peat Society and its constituent bodies is rapidly gaining and disseminating the relevant knowledge concerning the importance of mires on a regional, national and international scale.

PRESERVATION OF INTACT MIRE SYSTEMS

Until more information is available, the preservation of intact peatlands will be regarded by some as a noneconomic form of land use and as such must be justified. Peatlands are not in themselves regarded as areas of high amenity value and even the country lover who sings the praises of open rolling moorland often curses the saturated peat blanket underfoot. Thus the normal criteria used to convince official bodies to preserve large natural areas of landscape are of little or no use when it comes to mires. The case for the preservation of intact mire systems is therefore best argued on scientific grounds.

THE SCIENTIFIC CASE

The scientific case has in fact been made in the earlier chapters of this book, but some recapitulation seems appropriate as this point.

Peat is organic matter mainly of plant origin. Theoretically any plant community can form peat if given the right condition which is simply a saturated, deoxygenated habitat substrate. Few do owing to their intolerance of this template condition. However, anywhere in the world where water is retained on its way down from the catchment to the sea constitutes a template for the development of a peat producing ecosystem or mire (see Chapters 1 and 2).

All living organisms produce acidic substances as byproducts of their life processes. Any such acidic substances produced by organisms living in flowing, nutrient rich ground water will be neutralised by the bicarbonate present and will be flushed out of the system. As peat begins to accumulate within the mire system, the effect of flowing ground water will gradually be reduced and, as the process continues, the acidic substances will no longer be neutralised or flushed away but will accumulate within the system. Eventually, the surface of the peat will be raised above the level of the flowing ground water and an acidic, nutrient poor mire ecosystem will result. The hydrologic conditions and nutrient status (abiotic components) gradually undergo a change which is brought about by the storage of energy in the form of peat and this change is paralleled by a change in the biotic components of the ecosystem.

Detailed study by two peat schools indicates the existence of six or seven mire types which are floristically, ionically and hydrologically distinct (Figure 3.2). There is little doubt that these seven types represent no more than modes in a continuum of variation between the two extreme types. The main axis of this continuum is aligned with the hydroedaphic differences between the mires and can be related to the regulated biotic succession of the mire hydrosere (Chapter 3).

In any area of the world in which energy is stored in the form of peat, similar regulated biotic successions can take place, the relevant modifications of the template following the same basic pattern of hydroedaphic change. This basic hydroedaphic succession can be stabilised at any point allowing a normal 'Clementsian' succession to take place. A succession from 'simple' pioneer to 'complex' forest ecosystems. Figure 3.7 shows the ionic regime of a complete matrix of ecosystem types from one area. The matrix includes everything, from pioneer ecosystems developed in continuously flowing nutrient rich ground water, to complex mire forest existing on a minimal nutrient budget in which efficient mineral uptake, retention and cycling must play a significant role.

Mire ecosystems are simple in the following respects:

1. They are edaphically 'uniform', the main substrate matrix being organic matter produced by the biota themselves. Many of the complications of pedogenesis are therefore absent (Chapter 1)
2. They are trophically simplified, the decomposer chain being reduced to almost absent (Chapter 4)
3. They are the only type of ecosystem which record their own ontogeny. The record in the form of both macro and micro subfossils is often very complete and an accurate time scale may be determined using the techniques of pollen analysis and radiocarbon dating (Chapter 7).

Clarke's 'Data of Geochemistry' (Clarke, 1930) provides information on the range of ionic concentrations of natural ground waters on a world scale. Wherever peat accumulates there can exist series of ecosystems which are geochemically comparable. The mires of the world thus represent a matrix of biotically regulated 'chemostats' set against the background of macroclimatic variation; they therefore constitute ecological information par excellence.

It has been said that no two mires are alike, but this is untrue, as painstaking work has shown that the range of variation can be understood and meaningful divisive parameters erected. The permutations and combinations of cause and effect, muskeg, peatland, mires, torfowiska, the world matrix of peat producing ecosystems (Chapter 8) is not only the arena in which the mire ecologist finds his problems but the key with which he solves them. Added to this is the intrinsic importance of peat deposits as records of regional and local history. The history of vegetation and ecosystem development and of the use and abuse of the natural system by man is there for analysis (Chapter 7). The uniqueness of the mire information matrix is at once obvious.

Modern methods of exploitation (Chapter 9) are making the destruction of peatlands a rapid and catastrophic process. The matrix is thus being rapidly fragmented and in fact some parts of it have already been destroyed.

PROJECT TELMA

It was in this knowledge that the International Union for the Conservation of Nature initiated in 1966 an international project called TELMA, the aim of which was to develop co-operation for the conservation of peatlands for scientific research and education and for the protection of their wildlife. The International Biological Programme (I.B.P.) agreed to cosponsor the project with I.U.C.N. and the project subsequently developed under the aegis of the C.T. section of I.B.P. (see Nicholson and Douglas[15]).

The objects of Project TELMA are:

1. The preparation of a world list of peatland sites which are of international significance to science and the promotion of their conservation
2. The encouragement of communication and collaboration amongst research scientists investigating peatlands.

At the first meeting of Project TELMA held in 1967 reports were given by each national delegate on the particular threats to the peatlands in their countries. These are summarised below.

Particular Threats to Peatlands in some of the Countries under Review

Austria: There is little mechanised extraction. The main threats arise from reclamation for agriculture and the use of peat for balneotherapy.

Canada: Agricultural activity is significant in Canada between 45°N and 50°N. Further north, surveys are at present being carried out of the potential value to agriculture and forestry of virgin muskeg. The results of the surveys will also be used to allocate land for use for peat extraction and as wildlife reserves. It has been noted that in areas where cranberries and blueberries are grown commercially on peatlands they cause far less disturbance to the peat forming ecosystem than do other crops.

Land deterioration due to commercial peat extraction is becoming a significant threat from Winnipeg to Le Pas and in Newfoundland.

Concern has been growing about the effect of recent water diversion and flooding in river systems, particularly in the Quebec peninsula. These schemes are causing widespread hydrological disturbance and are seen as a major threat to large tracts of peatland. Damage by off road vehicular traffic, used in seismic survey, oil operations and forestry is increasing.

Czechoslovakia: Peat cutting and drainage constitute the main forms of exploitation in Czechoslovakia. Balneotherapy is also significant in some areas.

Denmark: Very few sites in Denmark remain undisturbed by peat cutting and drainage. Conservation is an urgent need.

Finland: It is estimated that by 1980 about 90% of Finland's peatland, which once covered 40% of the land surface (11 million hectares), will have been drained and planted. Drainage and cultivation have already almost wholly destroyed some of the most uncommon mire sites in southern Finland. It seems probable that virgin peatlands will disappear sooner in Finland than in other countries of the Boreal zone, since the national economy depends almost entirely on forestry.

The wet central area of domed mires are considered unsuitable for afforestation, but are seriously threatened by peat extraction. The consumption of peat for horticulture has increased considerably in recent years, and cut peat now serves a considerable export market.

Recently some northern peatlands have been covered by artificial lakes for hydroelectric schemes. Within the next few years, some 80 000 hectares will be threatened in this way, including the most extensive and famous peatland area of Finland, the Posoaapa, which covers about 40 000 hectares.

Great Britain: Drainage for agriculture and forestry, and eutrophication, constitute the major threat to British Peatlands. These activities, together with peat extraction for fuel and horticulture, are bringing about the rapid destruction of peatland sites.

The burning of surface vegetation, eutrophication of the ground water supply and the entry of toxic chemicals via atmosphere and ground water pollution all threaten changes of special content and the eventual destruction of peat forming ecosystems.

Irish Republic: All domed mires in Eire have suffered some degree of drainage and excavation at their margins, but many of them are so large that little damage has so far been caused. Similarly, in the remoter areas of western blanket mire, large domes and plains of undisturbed ombrotrophic peat are still to be found.

The largest peat exploiting body in Eire is Bord na Mona, the statutory Irish Peat Development Authority. Ireland has for centuries depended largely on peat for fuel, and today the Authority controls over 50 000 hectares of peatland with a view to industrial exploitation. Most of the larger unbroken areas of domed mire have already been acquired. It should be noted that the Bord also has a large research programme and is concerned about the problems of conservation.

Japan: The greatest continuing threat to Japan's peatlands is reclamation for rice production. In Hokkaido some of the mires have already been exploited, half of this amount being under cultivation.

An increasing threat, particularly near Tokyo, is heavy tourist pressure in scenic amenity areas: these include many valuable peatland sites which are threatened with considerable disturbance.

Netherlands: Of an estimated 180 000 hectares of original ombrotrophic mire, a mere 3600 have been left relatively undisturbed by extraction and by drainage for cultivation, though some areas once drained for buckwheat and later abandoned may be capable of regeneration in a

207

modified form.

Northern Ireland: A high proportion of the peatland which was formerly found at low altitudes has been greatly modified by draining, peat cutting and agricultural reclamation, particularly in the east of the province. Large areas of agricultural land have been reclaimed by draining fenland (south of Lough Neagh) and by stripping the upper moss peat and cultivating the surface thus exposed (Antrim). Hill peatland has also been exploited by intensive plough drainage, often with the application of lime.

About 50 000 hectares of peatland have so far been acquired for afforestation.

Sphagnum peat continues to be extracted for horticulture, and losses also occur from the burning of surface vegetation. Peat cutting for fuel is widespread, but does not at present threaten areas which have retained much scientific value.

Norway: Main threats are from agriculture and forestry, and extraction for the horticultural industry, especially plant pots made from compressed peat.

Poland: Almost 800 000 hectares (about 65%) of Polish peatlands have been exploited for economic purposes—particularly cultivation and afforestation: over half of the peatland in northern Poland is now covered by meadow and pasture. The chief danger arising from the agricultural exploitation of mires is the overdrying of peat deposits: a 'muck peat' soil is formed which quickly dries out, giving rise to a physiological drought and loss of fertility. Shrinkage of the deposits occurs: indeed, many shallow peatlands are in danger of complete destruction by drainage.

In the years following the second World War the use of cut peat as fuel increased rapidly until some 80 000 sites were exploited. Recently legislation has restricted peat cutting to a much lower level— but the damage from earlier exploitation is considerable, particularly as the sites were scattered over a large area.

Mire vegetation on disturbed sites has changed markedly through contiguous cutting and drainage, and eutrophication.

Sweden: Between 1880 and 1930 the exploitation of mires for agriculture expanded rapidly, with the encouragement of the Swedish Society for Peat Cultivation. After 1930 the agricultural exploitation of peatlands declined and has now virtually ceased. It has been estimated that reclamation affected about 200 000 hectares, although some of this area has been abandoned and is now reverting to mire conditions. At present, afforestation is the most serious threat to peatlands: it has been on the increase since the late nineteenth century, and today drainage operations affect some 15000-20000 hectares per annum. Some 3 million hectares—half the remaining peatland area of Sweden—is regarded as utilisable for afforestation, including all the remaining mires of south and south central Sweden. Drainage alone is not sufficient to sustain forest growth in these areas, and fertilisation is carried out to a large extent. It is feared that many typical Swedish mire types will be destroyed if unrestricted drainage and fertilisation are continued.

Turbary has declined in recent years and is now only a minor threat, but excavation of horticultural peat has increased rapidly to an estimated 1 million cubic metres per annum, and this development is continuing steadily.

U.S.A.: In some areas of the United States there is great agricultural pressure on peatlands, particularly in Florida where, as has already been mentioned, the drainage of swampland around the Everglades presents a serious threat. In some States cranberries are grown commercially, with comparatively little damage to peatlands.

Peat has never been used as fuel to any large extent, but the extraction of peat moss for horticulture, particularly near urban centres, is causing grave concern.

Growing centrifugal urbanisation is one of the major threats; and there is pressure for the use of peatlands for amenities, such as a new airport for New York on the New Jersey Great Swamp.

Yugoslavia: The major threat to the remaining mires in Yugoslavia, since they are too small for commercial or agricultural exploitation, is tourist pressure: some concern has been expressed about indiscriminate path making and amenity development on these sites.

In the light of these reports it was decided to prepare a world list of sites which will, as far as possible, make up the 'international series' as follows:

1. A primary list of sites representative of a series according to their hydromorphology, vegetation structure, and, if known, peat structure
2. A list of sites required for research of international significance, (research sites)
3. A list of sites of international importance by reason of their being especially well documented, biologically, stratigraphically, archaeologically (monument sites)
4. A list of sites of international importance as habitats for interesting species and communities of plants and animals.

When the Telma list is complete and if all the recommendations for reserves are instituted there are still a number of problems regarding long term conservation.

Succession The process of natural succession must in time change the nature of the mire communities in any reserve. The problem is whether to institute management of the system to maintain the *status quo*, that is to create and preserve an 'unnatural' system. The classic case of this is one of the first mire reserves created in Wicken Fen, an area of rheotrophic mire in England which is only maintained in a 'natural' state because water is continuously pumped into the system. The alternative is to allow succession to take its course, thus maintaining a natural situation at the expense of loss of some of its diversity.

Once it is accepted that only a limited number of sites can be preserved *sensu stricto,* the importance of the rehabilitation of areas from which the peat has been removed must be realised. This is especially true where the commercial value of the resultant cutaway (the area from which the peat has been removed) is low. It is suggested, therefore, that the following considerations should be built into the planning of all peat winning operations, however large or small.

1. Ecological survey of the mire system prior to exploitation, as a basis for rational use

2. Maintenance of the genetical diversity of the mire system by:

a. Careful exploitation and/or complete preservation of one section of the mire

b. Maintenance of high ground water tables in all cutaways by blocking the effluent drains once cutting has finished. This is a simple and cheap operation while the machinery is still on site

c. Leaving the site with as much topographical diversity as possible. This is particularly true where machinery, especially milling methods, are used which tend to leave large flat expanses devoid of both plants and animals and take a very long time to rehabilitate. If it is possible the last two cuts should be by hand or sod cutting machines and some peat baulks should be left. Thus the bottom of the cutaway will be of uneven relief, providing a diversity of habitat for wildlife and centres for recolonisation of the vegetation once they have been reflooded.

An excellent example of such collaboration between the peat winning concern and the conservationists has been described by Rogers and Bellamy[16]. The site is a lowland domed ombrotrophic mire complex in Yorkshire, England. The 3500 acres of peatlands which are collectively known as Thorne Waste have been subject to drainage and to agricultural and peat winning operations for more than 300 years. For well over 70 years the peat works have been on a massive scale and are today highly mechanised. At least one cut has been taken from over 95% of the area and none of the contemporary mire surface can be called natural. Nevertheless, a survey by Skidmore[17] reported the existence of a rich flora and fauna in the area which includes much of the genetic diversity of the original peatlands as indicated by stratigraphical analysis. An ecological survey was carried out with a view to conservation and the peat winning operations have been modified accordingly.

The value of the site to education and research and hence the importance of the above cooperation in planning is made clear when it is realised that within a radius of 50 km of the mire there are 11 major towns with a total population of 2 million, and that four of these towns have Universities.

Eutrophication and Pollution

The effects of these factors can be brought together under three main headings.

1. Eutrophication, that is enrichment by nutrients of ground waters by sewage pollution, and by agricultural practices such as liming and the use of fertilisers in the catchment

2. Eutrophication of the rain by atmospheric contamination from industry, conurbations, agriculture and civil engineering operations.

3. Pollution of mire waters by the addition of toxic geochemicals, heavy metals etc. and herbicides, pesticides, defoliants, detergents etc. either via the ground water or the rain water.

Although the effects of these factors on mires are not immediate, as in the case of draining and cutting, they are nevertheless very serious in that the nature of the mires exposed to such threats will, in time, change radically. The situation is the more serious in that eutrophication and pollution are much more difficult to control than direct physical disturbance. It is thus clear that the reserve unit should be the mire complex plus its catchment system.

The importance of ombrotrophic mires as natural monitoring stations for recording changes in the airborne load of heavy metals and other pollutants (see Pheeney and Radforth[18]) must be emphasised. Work is already far advanced in using the moss *Hylocomium splendens* which is a common component of the vegetation of ombrotrophic mires to map the distribution of atmospheric pollution by lead in Scandinavia.

The heavy metal content, and uptake characteristics of *Sphagnum* spp. are being investigated in many laboratories so that a series of monitoring stations may be instituted.

Public Pressure

Population pressures will clearly increase and will constitute an increasing threat to peatland areas especially those near centres of population or tourism. Mire communities are especially susceptible to trampling and some may be radically altered by quite small numbers of people walking over the surface. The use of mire lakes for swimming and other water sports are often focal centres for such disturbance and these uses should be strictly controlled in reserves.

Included under this heading must also be the increased use of natural ecosystem as open air laboratories, both for teaching and research. Where regular access for teaching and research is essential corduroy roads, duckboarding and raised walkways should be constructed. These have been installed with great success on mire types of all sorts and the damage has thus been successfully controlled.

EPILOGUE

Since the initiation of project TELMA in 1967 international concern regarding the conservation of natural resources has increased many fold, and has found a place in the agenda and working papers of most governmental and international meetings, concerned with the welfare of man. The success of project TELMA was evidenced at the 4th International Peat Congress held in Helsinki in 1972 where not only were many papers presented which contained sections on conservation but the 1st volume of the Proceedings was entitled *Virgin Peatlands Conservation and Terminology.*

REFERENCES

1. DEEVEY, E.S. Bogs. *Scientific American,* October (1958).
2. CONWAY, V.M. and MILLAR, A. The hydrology of some peat covered catchments in the Northern Pennines. *J. Inst. Wat. Engrs.* **14,** 415-424 (1960).
3. MALAK, A. *River Training.* Warsaw, 216 (1956).
4. DACHNOWSKI-STOKES, A.P. 'Peat Deposits in U.S.A.' *Handbuch Moorkunde* **VII,** 1-40 (1933).
5. KULCZYNSKI, S. Torfowiska Polesia 1 and 2 Krawkow (1939).
6. BADEN, W. and EGGLESMAN, R. (1968). 'The hydrologic budget of the Highbogs in the Atlantic Region.' *Proc. 3rd Int. Peat Cong. Quebec,* 200-219 (1968).
7. TANSLEY, A.G. *The British Islands and their vegetation.* Cambridge, 259-264 (1939).
8. PRUS-CHAKINSKI, T.M. 'Shrinkage of peatlands due to drainage operations.' *J. Inst. Wat. Engrs.,* **16,** 436-448 (1962).
9. WALTER, H.L. 'Carrot and Onion Production on Bradford Marsh. *Farm Economics.* Co-operatives and Statistics Branch Ontario Dept. of Agric. and Food, Jan. 1-36 (1968).
10. BOWER, M.M. 'Peat erosion in the Pennines.' *Adv. Sc., London* **64,** 323-31 (1960).
11. FRITTON, A.H. 'Farming of Lancashire Mossland.' *Proc. Meres and Mires Conference,* 31. The Nature Conservancy, London (1965).
12. IVANOV, E.S. 'Combustion of Milled Peat.' *Proc. 4th Int. Peat Cong. Helsinki,* **2,** 139-147 (1972).

13. TOLPA, S. 'Stimulators and inhibitors insolated from Peat.' *Proc. 4th Int. Peat Cong. Helsinki,* 31-37 (1972).

14. ATKINS, P.S. 'Soil-less Compost Investigations at Levington Research Station.' *Proc. 3rd Int. Peat Cong. Quebec,* 246-250 (1968).

15. NICHOLSON, E.M. and DOUGLAS, G.L. *IBP/CT: Progress Report. Int. Biol. Proc. Lond.* 97-128 (1971).

16. ROGERS, S.A. and BELLAMY, D.J. Peat Exploitation and conservation: a case history. *Proc. 4th Int. Peat Cong. Helsinki,* 1, 219-233 (1972).

17. SKIDMORE, P. '50 years later another look at Thorne Waste.' *Naturalist* **914,** 81-87 (1970).

18. PHEENEY, P.E. and RADFORTH, N.W. *Proc. 4th Int. Peat Cong. Helsinki,* **1,** 203 (1972).

213

Index

214

216